Brother Carl

By Susan Sontag

Novels
THE BENEFACTOR

DEATH KIT

Essays
AGAINST INTERPRETATION

TRIP TO HANOI

STYLES OF RADICAL WILL

Filmscripts
DUET FOR CANNIBALS

BROTHER CARL

Brother Carl

A filmscript by SUSAN SONTAG

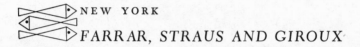

NEW YORK
FARRAR, STRAUS AND GIROUX

FIRST PRINTING, 1974

Published simultaneously in Canada
by Doubleday Canada Ltd., Toronto
Printed in the United States of America
Designed by Herb Johnson

Library of Congress Cataloging in Publication Data
Sontag, Susan.
    Brother Carl.
    I. Brother Carl. [Motion picture]
PN1997.B764S6   1974   791.43'7   72-82949

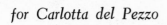

for Carlotta del Pezzo

March 1969. The day after I had checked the first print of *Duet for Cannibals* back from the laboratory, it was screened for Göran Lindgren, president of Sandrew Film & Teater AB, the company that had produced the film. He saw it alone, at ten o'clock on a Saturday morning in the empty Sandrew office building; I came ten minutes after the screening started and spent the next hour and a half pacing off the corridor. In the time since I had first come to Sweden, on his unexpected invitation, in July 1968, to make a film, Lindgren and I had seldom met; he had never appeared on the set, come to the rushes, or turned up during the editing and mixing. What he said in the corridor after that screening took about a minute. He liked *Duet for Cannibals*, he told me. I was "welcome" in Sweden the following year to make another film. We shook hands, he turned toward his office, and I went into the street to look for the sun. A few days later, without seeing Lindgren again, I left Stockholm. So accustomed was I by then to the laconic, shy, spectacularly honest Swedes that it never occurred to me to wonder if I needed a contract or a letter to be sure that Sandrew really meant to produce my second film. And, of course, I didn't.

Early January 1971. The first print of *Brother Carl* has just come back from the laboratory. A different screening room, for Sandrew has new offices now, but the same ritual: Lindgren inside, alone, the first to see the finished film, and me, late on purpose, alone in the corridor. End of screening. Some polite words about *Brother Carl*, a question about when I am leaving for France, and a handshake. No inquiry about my next film project, which does not surprise me, since there was a rumor circulating in the company well before the shooting began that Lindgren wants Sandrew to lay off film production altogether for a while. He turns toward his office, and I go down into the street—though not to look for the sun. In Stockholm in January, even noon is still night. I find that I'm relieved not to be asked back. That particular, intense, "Swedish" trip inside my head is over. I can start making films elsewhere: France perhaps; soon, I hope, the United States.

Brother Carl took longer to write than *Duet for Cannibals*. After the première of *Duet for Cannibals* in May 1969, I spent most of the summer in Italy. I redid the new film in my head several times, confident that I could write it out quickly. Only as I started putting *Brother Carl* down on paper, when I returned to New York in September, did I realize how many tough questions about film narration and construction the making of *Duet for Cannibals* had opened up for me. I also had the benefit of an interlocutor this time. Throughout most of the autumn my friend Florence Malraux participated intellectually in the genesis of *Brother Carl* and gave the emerging script several hours each day of passionate, skeptical, and delicate criticisms. I want here to express my deep and loving gratitude for that dialogue we had together.

The first draft was finished in December. I sent it on to Lindgren and to the minority producer, Harry Schein of the Swedish Film Institute, before arriving in Stockholm in mid-January 1970. During a two-week stay, I put together the crew (many had worked with me on *Duet for Cannibals*), chose some of the locations (the hotel, Martin's summer house, the abandoned fort, the abandoned factory), and spoke with actors. Gunnel Lindblom agreed to play Lena, as I had hoped, for the part had been written with her in mind. It took a long, hard discussion with Lindgren to convince him to let me shoot in black-and-white, which he was understandably reluctant to do since this now severely limits a film's commercial possibilities. I simply could not imagine *Brother Carl*—a winter's tale, to be shot in late summer: far north—as a color film. As I saw it in my head, it was a film in black-and-white, more accurately, black-*to*-white images: about a present haunted by an untellable "black" act of corruption that lies in the past, transfixed by an unmerited "white" act of healing that waits in the future.

When I left Stockholm at the beginning of February 1970, I stopped off in Paris, hoping that I could persuade Laurent Terzieff (an actor I'd admired for years but had never met) to accept the role of Carl. I discovered that he had gone on tour for the month. The phone call that finally reached him was to the backstage of a theatre in a small city whose name I've forgotten, an hour before curtain time. Apologetic, and forced to shout (the connection being up to the usual Paris-to-provinces standard) in my far from perfect French, I tried to explain who I was, that I wanted him to be in a film, and that I hoped to come to see him that week, wherever he would be. To my astonishment, he replied that my trip wouldn't be necessary, since he knew that he would like to work with me. Two minutes after the start of our conversation, without giving me time even to tell him the theme of the film or what his role would be, and undeterred by my warning that he (like everyone working on the film) would be paid next to nothing, I had his promise to put aside three months to come to Sweden. Although I had been prepared by Lindgren to receive arbitrary gifts of trust, Terzieff's two-minute consent, blind, over the telephone (we did not meet until two months later), had nothing of the stately tone of Lindgren's one minute in the corridor the previous March. No one could be more un-Swedish than ascetic, exacting, ardent, generous Laurent—who was to be, quite simply, perfect in his understanding of Carl. More confident in the script now that I knew Terzieff would play Carl, I went back to New York and rewrote it once more.

It was Laurent Terzieff who first observed—when I sent him the script a month later—that in the tormented history of Martin and Carl I was evoking the legendary relationship between Diaghilev and Nijinsky. I told him he was right, and I know it helped Terzieff to believe that in the weeks he spent preparing for the role before he arrived in Stockholm in July. I wasn't telling the truth. My distant real-life models were a more contemporary director (theatre, not ballet) and his holy fool. But even they were only the vaguest of starting points for *Brother Carl*. The characters that became Martin and Carl are people who have lived for decades inside my head—emblems of the dramaturgy of silence (or voluntary mutism) that has been a recurrent theme in my life and in my novels as well as my films. Silence haunts *The Benefactor*, not only as an option stated in the plot but, more important, in the off-centered loquacity of the narrator (which gives an oppressive weight to all that he does *not* tell). Voluntary mutism is what tempts Diddy throughout the long meditation on dying which is the argument of *Death Kit*; and as he makes his pilgrim's progress toward death, Hester's blindness is another, transposed form of silence. In *Duet for Cannibals*, the catalytic member of the quartet, Francesca, refuses to speak. And the Francesca figure reappears in *Brother Carl*, doubled: as the almost mute Carl and as the autistic child. Looking back now, I recognize in Martin a new version of the psychological fascist in *Duet for Cannibals*. Martin is a Bauer past his prime; a Bauer who has already wreaked the maximum amount of damage; a Bauer who, in a state of exhaustion, revulsion, and weary cynicism, has lost his appetite for playing games and even hopes to behave decently.

Out of the script for *Duet for Cannibals*, which was written in English, I chose to make a Swedish-language film. I had engaged three gifted Swedish actors who all spoke English fluently. But I knew they would not have the same freedom or expressiveness if they acted their roles in English. No actor, however talented, retains his or her full range in a second language. (For the fourth member of the quartet, the Italian actress Adriana Asti, the question was irrelevant; since she spoke neither English nor Swedish, she would in either case still have had to learn her relatively few lines phonetically.) So the script was translated, which did wonders for my hitherto lazy progress in learning Swedish. English remained the language of the set —the language of all discussions with the crew and the actors (except for Adriana Asti)—but the actors spoke Swedish when they were before the camera.

With *Brother Carl*, I started with the same elements: Swedish actors who, along with Geneviève Page, spoke fair to excellent English; and Laurent Terzieff, who spoke neither English nor Swedish and would, whatever my decision, have to learn his part phonetically, as Adriana Asti had done in *Duet for Cannibals*. This time, I did not have the script translated into Swedish. I decided to exploit the very peculiarity of my situation—an American director, working with a mostly bi-lingual cast, in a country in which English is the official second language. By asking the actors to perform in English, I knew that I was abridging their range and diminishing their comfort. But I wanted them to work from within that very handicap. Whereas in *Duet for Cannibals* I had simply aimed at getting "good" (i.e., professional, subtle) performances out of the actors, I asked something less traditional from the actors in *Brother Carl*. I wanted to incorporate as a *formal* element in the film the very difficulties they would have sometimes in speaking English—the play of accents, their hesitations, mis-placed rhythms, stiffnesses.

The material of *Brother Carl* (unlike *Duet for Cannibals*) seemed well suited to this kind of experiment, since the plot itself turned on the dilemmas of speaking, of being silent—of finding it hard (or questionable) to speak at all. This notion of the acting completed what I had been trying to do when I wrote the actors' lines. The dialogue in *Brother Carl* is much more consistently "de-naturalistic" than that of *Duet for Cannibals*, which alternates between scraps of everyday banalities and passages of schizoid-like declamation. In *Brother Carl*, the "interference" of everyday life is bleached out, as far as I could do that and still stay within the bounds of some kind of psychological realism. In successive drafts of *Brother Carl*, most "naturalistic" touches were cut—for the same reason that I decided not to let any of the characters be seen smoking. (Considered as "real" people, both Lena and Karen would undoubtedly be chain smokers—like Tomas in *Duet for Can-*

nibals.) The actors' accents in English would confirm (rather than "distance" even further) this elliptical, formal kind of dialogue.

I went to Stockholm for the first ten days of June 1970 to confer with the set designer and finish the casting, and returned to start full preparations in early July. Shooting began on August 3 and continued, over a period of eight weeks, through September 26: forty-six shooting days. We shot in black-and-white 35 mm. film with one Arriflex camera and recorded the dialogue with a Nagra—but only as guide track, because I had decided to rerecord everything, after the film was edited, in a sound studio.

From the second week of shooting on, I began working nights with Lars Hagström in the Sandrew editing room, and when the shooting ended we already had a rough cut of most of the film. The final editing was done in October, during which I also worked with the composer Torbjörn Lundqvist (whom Hagström had recommended) on the music. The dubbing and mixing were done in November and December. All the actors dubbed themselves; even six-year-old Pernilla Ålfeldt, who had never acted before and knew no English, managed Anna's flow of laughter and single line at the end of the film ("He's heavy!") very creditably.

In the post-shooting work on *Brother Carl*, the most interesting part for me concerned the sound. Except for the way music is used, the knocking motif, and the structure of what Tomas hears on the tape recorder, the sound track of *Duet for Cannibals*—considered as layers of sound—is neither original nor particularly interesting. All the actors' lines and most of the sound effects were those that had been recorded during the shooting—embedded in the subliminally fuzzy aural atmosphere that fills every "real" space, however quiet. The result was a wholly serviceable, functional sound. (It was remarkably clean, too, considering that we filmed entirely on locations in and around the city, not in a studio—every good take a victory over the menace of a rumbling stomach, a passing car, a neighbor's crying child, a low-flying airplane.) But it was a dry sound; and, most important, it added little, formally, to the film. In *Brother Carl*, I wanted to render the sound elements essential to the structure of the film, not just to its narrative sense. With the very best "direct" sound I would still have had only a two-dimensional sketch of what a formally *active* sound track could contain. Everything had to be done (or redone) in a studio, after the film was edited.

As the actors came, one by one, to rerecord their lines, I asked them sometimes to imitate what they heard on the guide track, sometimes to give a contrasting reading. Not limited to using what had come out in the single inspiration of the take that was best all-round, I could manipulate the contrast between their "expressive" and their "artificial" ways of speaking. After this final stage of work with the actors came several weeks re-creating the effects. As in *Duet for Cannibals*, these were commonplace (doors opening and closing, objects dropping, footsteps, the crackling of a fire, the dial tone), but in *Brother Carl* they were re-done so as to have an abrasive, partly artificial sound—acquiring a presence in the film that sound effects recorded direct can never have. I wanted to use the effects like the actors' accents in English—as an abstract, musical element; not just for sense.

In late December, mixing the film, I worked to set up a certain play among the three elements: dialogue, sound effects, and music. Some of the music was mixed "too loud." Occasionally, I covered an actor's line with an effect to make the line harder to hear. I never stopped thinking of the dialogue as important. But I also wanted to include, as a formal element in the film, a certain *resistance* to the dialogue—almost like a physical resistance or obstacle—which testifies to the way speaking as such is put in question in the situation narrated in *Brother Carl*. Against language itself, which is a kind of colonialization of the feelings, the film evokes the deeper but more dangerous contact between people that is created by the challenge of a mute presence, by an apparent inability (or unwillingness) to speak.

Brother Carl tells a story, linear in form, about real people stripped down to their imaginary psychology.

Though not conscious of it when writing the script, I now see that *Brother Carl* starts from the same plot form as *Duet for Cannibals:* a tale of couples. But the range and the tone are very different. In the relatively simple design of *Duet for Cannibals,* one couple (Francesca and Arthur Bauer), solidly if bizarrely united, metaphorically devour and then regurgitate another, younger couple (Ingrid and Tomas), whose life together is failing. *Brother Carl* also shows two couples—one already failed (Lena and Martin, divorced five years before the film's action begins) and another who continue together in unconsummated estrangement (Karen and Peter Sandler). At the beginning of *Brother Carl,* Karen and Peter are in somewhat the same sterile, discontented state of semi-failure as the younger Ingrid and Tomas. (Karen is near forty and Peter is in his early thirties, while both Ingrid and Tomas are in their middle to late twenties.) But the two couples are not simply left to intersect with each other, as in *Duet for Cannibals.* For they are not alone. On each side there is a "child," a child who is too angry or too wounded to speak. Martin has his genius protégé, who used to dance. The Sandlers have their young daughter, whom all sounds interest except words. The introduction of that refusal—that pathos and pain incarnated by the "child"—generates the more complex interchanges of this couple story. While nobody in *Brother Carl* (unlike *Duet for Cannibals*) is shown as able to make love physically, the characters do try to care for each other. Some have already surrendered their capacity to give and to receive, however. Their exchanges of energy are not, basically, "cannibalistic"—only, for the most part, futile or misplaced. Lena, who is strong and decent and deserves to live, makes the mistake of attaching her life to the struggle to reclaim love—and loses. Karen, who is weak and selfish and hardly merits anything in her own right, is rewarded.

The thematic resemblances between *Duet for Cannibals* and *Brother Carl,* such as I can detect now, only confirm my pleasure in what I understood earlier to be the differences between the two films. What counts most for me about *Brother Carl* is that it takes a step beyond *Duet for Cannibals*: the spatial relations within the shots are subtler, the editing is more intelligent, the use of sound is more sophisticated, and the connections among the characters are more complex. It is a handsomer film (in terms of lighting, set design, suppleness of the camera) than *Duet for Cannibals*; it is also, probably because my feelings are more exposed in it, sometimes clumsier. In this sense, *Brother Carl* stands in somewhat the same relation to *Duet for Cannibals* as my second to my first novel. Both *The Benefactor* and *Duet for Cannibals* have in common a considerable emotional reticence, a recoil from pain that masks itself as humor. In *Brother Carl*, as in *Death Kit*, pain is more visible; no one is being ironic at the expense of his or her own suffering. I don't mean that I prefer the second film to the first, any more than I prefer the second novel to the first. But I know that, as the aim of *Brother Carl* (like that of *Death Kit*) was more ambitious, the risks taken far greater, the results more uneven and less harmonious, those passages in *Brother Carl* which do work surpass anything I was able to accomplish in *Duet for Cannibals*.

From the beginning, when I first imagined *Brother Carl*, the center was the miracle. The narrative was to build toward two miracles: one that does not take place (the resurrection of Lena), and one that does (the healing of Anna) in whatever terms a miracle is thinkable now. Though the miracle Carl does manage to bring off is far from the "traditional" miracle pictured in Dreyer's *Ordet*, which takes place within the setting of a still pious, rural society, I feel strongly influenced by my memory of *Ordet*. I saw the film only once, about fifteen years ago, and doubt that I remember it accurately. But that film, probably greatly transformed by the willfulness of memory, has remained all these years as a kind of ideal experience of my imagination—along with Dreyer's last film, *Gertrud*, and the Bunraku theatre, and the films of Jean-Marie Straub.

The only interesting action in life is a miracle or the failure to perform a miracle; and miracles are the only subject of profound interest left for art. I say this as someone who has tried to perform a kind of miracle (that effort being the deepest personal source of *Brother Carl*) or, more modestly, to help a miracle come to pass. When I started to write the script, I was in the throes of that effort. The week after the end of shooting, in Rome, I learned I had failed. That failure has not destroyed my belief in miracles.

SUSAN SONTAG

Paris
June 1972

Brother Carl

CREDITS

WRITTEN AND DIRECTED BY: *Susan Sontag*
PRODUCED BY: *Sandrew Film & Teater AB and Svenska Filminstitutet*
EXECUTIVE PRODUCER: *Göran Lindgren*
PRODUCTION MANAGER: *Peter Hald*
PHOTOGRAPHY: *Rune Ericson / Björn Thermaenius*
SOUND: *Ulf Darin / Björn Öberg*
SET DESIGNER: *Charles Delattre*
UNIT MANAGER: *Britt Olsson*
ASSISTANT TO THE DIRECTOR: *Brita Werkmäster*
CONTINUITY: *Marianne Johnson*
CLOTHING AND PROPERTIES: *Inger Persson*
MAKE-UP: *Tina Johansson*
ELECTRICIAN: *Ulf Björk*
GRIPS: *Ted Lindahl / Ragge Waaranperä*

EDITOR: *Lars Hagström*
MUSIC COMPOSED BY: *Torbjörn Lundqvist*
MUSIC PERFORMED BY: *The Saulesco String Quartet / Claes Hellman*, flute / *Mona Liljienqvist*, violin / *Björn Liljienqvist*, percussion / *The Quiet Grave*
LABORATORY: *AB Film-Labor*
MIXING: *Berndt Frithiof / Kjell Westman (AB Film-Teknik)*

3

CAST

CARL NORÉN: *Laurent Terzieff*
KAREN SANDLER: *Geneviève Page*
LENA HOLMBERG: *Gunnel Lindblom*
MARTIN ERICSSON: *Keve Hjelm*
PETER SANDLER: *Torsten Wahlund*
ANNA SANDLER: *Pernilla Ålfeldt*

NOTE

The present script includes eight sequences (3, 4, 14, 26, 53, 54, 56, 57), as well as several parts of sequences, which I shot but dropped during the editing, and four sequences (44, 45, 46, and 47) which were never shot. These are set off by the signs ▼ and ▲.

The length of the film is ninety-five minutes.

The large (3′ x 3′) blowups of photographs in Martin's cottage (particularly conspicuous in sequences 16, 41, and 45) are of wax sculptures—life-size anatomical models—made in the last century by Gaetano Zumbo. The originals are in the Museo della Specola in Florence; they are reproduced in the book by Mario Bucci, *Anatomia Come Arte* (Firenze: Edizione d'Arte Il Fiorino, 1969), Plates IV, VI, XXII, and XXVI.

Brother Carl had its first public screening at the Cannes Film Festival, under the auspices of La Quinzaine des Réalisateurs, in May 1971. It is distributed by New Yorker Films in the United States. In France it has been released under the title *Les Gémeaux*.

Pre-credit sequence

1. Living room of Sandler apartment, and outside fort at Rindö. Day

Medium shot. The lower part of one wall of the living room of an upper-middle-class Stockholm apartment. At the top of the frame, a stereo tuner and turntable, which sit on a large white wooden cabinet; to the right is a modern easy chair covered with a striped material. The sound of a clock, ticking loudly. A child of six—ANNA—wearing only her white underpants, enters briskly from screen right (her back to the camera), holding a clock. She opens the cabinet door, gets inside, and closes the door. We continue to hear the clock ticking, slightly muffled. No other sound. Moments later, a woman enters slowly from the right. We see only the lower part of her body (she is wearing pants); the legs pause for a moment before the closed cabinet door. Then she comes into full view as she sits down on the chair with evident weariness. It is ANNA's mother, KAREN SANDLER. The shot continues for a few moments more, as KAREN sits without moving, her face showing her bitter sense of helplessness. The loud ticking of the clock continues.

Cut to a long shot of a tall, thin man—CARL NORÉN—opening out the two heavy metal doors of a small recessed area in the outer wall of the abandoned fort at Rindö. CARL wears a white turtleneck sweater, grey pants, and black shoes (no socks, as throughout the film). The harsh noise of the doors opening; the distant sound of water.

7

A closer shot: we see, from CARL's point of view, ANNA sitting inside, clasping her knees. She is wearing a short dress and shoes. She looks up calmly, impassively.

Another shot of CARL. He smiles ruefully, and shakes his head. Then he bends down and with some difficulty gets inside with her. The space is quite small for the two of them. He has to pull his legs in after him. He starts to close the two doors.

Another shot, very long (from the right): at a distance, we see CARL's hand pulling the doors shut from the inside, and hear more faintly the clanging sound the metal makes. The camera stays a few moments more on the façade of the old fort. Natural "atmosphere" sounds. Then blackness and silence.

Credits. In white letters, smallish-size type face, on the black screen. Music.

2. *Living room of Sandler apartment. Evening*

Long shot. In the foreground, PETER SANDLER and ANNA sit on the couch (couch A). ANNA squirms a little. PETER's arm rests heavily across his daughter's shoulders. PETER is a clean-cut, boyish-looking man in his early thirties. He wears a dark suit, white shirt, grey tie. ANNA is wearing only her white underwear. The couch is covered with the same striped material as the chair seen in the first shot of sequence 1. Part of the living room as well as the dining room with which it connects are visible in the background. It is clearly a spacious, comfortable apartment, furnished in conventional "modern" taste. The walls are white. There should be a terrace visible, to help establish that we are in the center of the city.

Medium long shot, from behind the couch. ANNA pulls away from PETER's hold and gets up. She lurches across the room, past another couch (couch B), to the telephone, picks up the receiver and listens to the dial tone.

Medium shot of ANNA avidly listening to the dial tone. By this shot, the audience should suspect that she is autistic. (Though she does not use or respond to language, she is not deaf.) The dial tone is very loud.

Low-angle shot of PETER on couch A, grimacing. He gets up. The camera follows as he goes over to the child. The dial tone gets louder. He bends over and, with an edge of distaste, tries to take the phone from her and replace it on the hook. ANNA struggles to hold on to the phone. He gets it away from her, and picks her up and sits her down with him on couch B. (Hanging above couch B is a reproduction of Magritte's "The Red Model.") ANNA stops struggling and stares straight ahead. PETER looks at her, frustrated and depressed.

Time to go to bed.

As PETER speaks to the child, he mouths the words with special distinctness and then makes a pantomime of putting his head on a pillow and falling asleep. ANNA pays no attention to her father. He goes on with the imitation, snoring. Glancing at the child, he sees that he is still not getting anywhere. We hear KAREN's voice. She has just returned home.

KAREN

(*Off*) Just do it! Don't announce it!

PETER looks up. ANNA does not.

Medium shot of KAREN standing on the threshold on the other side of the living room. Her hair is messy and her clothes a little disheveled; she is wearing suède pants and a white blouse, and carries a suède jacket slung over one shoulder. The camera backs away as she walks unsteadily to the couch. Now both PETER and ANNA are in the shot. KAREN looks down at her daughter, smiles painfully, but doesn't pick her up. PETER seems much more relieved than reproachful. KAREN is pacing in front of the couch.

PETER

I've been so worried. Where were you?

KAREN turns to PETER.

KAREN

I had a little scene with the police. Want to hear about it?

Having wriggled out of PETER's grasp, ANNA stands up and then steps up to stand on the back of the couch, pressing herself against the wall. (The lower half of the Magritte reproduction is in the shot.) She stares ahead, not looking at either of her parents.

                    PETER
Not in front of the child. Please!

                    KAREN
You think she can understand us?

                    PETER
She can *see* you. You look terrible.

KAREN looks at the child, then down at PETER still sitting on the couch.

                    KAREN
Then take her away, damn you!

She walks away. PETER gets up rapidly, follows her. Next to couch A he grabs her roughly by the shoulders. The camera is close to them.

PETER
Look at you! What are you doing to yourself?

KAREN submits to PETER's grasp; looking into his eyes, she replies with quiet bitterness.

KAREN
Aren't you glad she can't understand us?

* ▼   Medium shot of couch B. ANNA still standing precariously, unmoving, her bare back against the wall. PETER enters the shot from the left and takes his daughter in his arms. She struggles violently, kicking and clawing at his shirt. Camera pans with him as he carries her from the room.

3. Rocky shore. Day

Very long shot of CARL, from behind. He is standing on the rocks, fishing. His movements are slow and give the impression of being both overdeliberate and weightless. He wears a loose shirt and trousers rolled up to his mid-calves; he is barefoot. Low sound of water. Music.

4. Living room of Sandler apartment. Minutes later than sequence 2

Medium shot of PETER reentering the room. The camera follows him as he crosses to KAREN, who is standing at the open door that leads onto the terrace. He stands behind her, and kisses her cheek.

* The triangles indicate sequences. and parts of sequences either not filmed or dropped in the final editing.

PETER
I'm sorry.

KAREN doesn't move.

PETER
Did anything happen to the car?

KAREN doesn't move.

KAREN
I'm going to change.

She still doesn't move. PETER puts his arm around her.

PETER
Don't . . . You look fine.

KAREN turns, looks at him blankly. Sound of the telephone ringing.

Full shot: the camera is near the wall opposite the terrace. KAREN makes a dash for the phone and answers it. PETER is now in the rear of the shot. (In the following conversation, we hear KAREN's voice only, not even the unintelligible sound of the other person—it is LENA—talking.)

KAREN
Hello (*impersonal*) . . . Oh, hello (*warm*) . . . What's happening?

She picks up the phone, takes a few steps, smiling sarcastically at PETER (now no longer in the shot). KAREN takes the phone, which has a long cord, to couch B while she continues to talk. The camera pans with her.

KAREN
Fine . . . No, nothing's wrong. Why do you ask? . . . No, not especially . . . Yes . . . Why not?

13

KAREN lies down, kicks off her shoes.

> KAREN
>
> Sure I can come . . . Longer if you like.

Full shot of PETER (from KAREN's point of view). Furious, he leaves the living room. We hear the front door of the apartment slam shut.

> KAREN
>
> (*Off*) It was Peter . . . No . . . No, I'll tell you to-morrow.

High-angle shot of KAREN stretched out on the couch. As she talks, she unbuttons her blouse.

> KAREN
>
> No, I *don't* have a headache. Do you think because you have a headache I should have one too?
>
> > (*Pause*)
>
> Sorry . . . Yes . . .
>
> > (*Pause*)
>
> Yes . . . A little drunk. A very little, little, little . . .

She giggles. Then her expression changes. She is taking her blouse off, shifting the receiver from one hand to the other.

> KAREN
>
> No, I don't need anything . . . I'm not sick to my stomach.

KAREN unfastens her belt with one hand and throws it on the floor.

> KAREN
>
> Please don't mother me, Lena!

Low-angle medium shot, taken from the side of the couch, of the length of KAREN's body (except her head). She slips off her pants.

KAREN

(*Off*) I know you mean well.

Long shot (camera is near the front door). KAREN is in the rear of the shot, lying on the couch in her bra and underpants. PETER opens the door softly and enters the shot. He's carrying a newspaper. KAREN goes on with her phone call, but her voice is vague.

KAREN

Did you tell him?

The camera follows PETER as he comes over to the couch. He sits on the floor beside KAREN and puts his head on her stomach. Still holding the receiver to her ear with her right hand, she caresses PETER's hair with her left hand, without looking down at his face.

KAREN

What? . . . Sure I'm listening . . .

KAREN closes her eyes, continues to stroke PETER's hair.

KAREN

Listen . . . you're right. (*Laughs.*) I am beginning to fall asleep.

KAREN takes the receiver away from her ear and lets her right arm hang over the side of the couch. We hear a click, then the dial tone.

5. *Small theatre. Next day*

Medium close-up of a young man getting a sharp punch in the jaw (we see only his head and a fist). He falls out of the image to the right and we hear a loud sound, like someone tripping over a garbage can. The camera pulls back to a medium shot as another young man (we see him from the waist up) rushes across the frame from left to right. More loud noises. They come back into the shot just as the second man gets punched, then fall out together to the left. (Rock music throughout the sequence, but muffled—as it sounds when coming over a cheap transistor radio a room away.)

Long shot of the small stage area. (It is a theatre-in-the-round in Stockholm.) The two who are fighting are both in their late teens or early twenties, similar in build and coloring; both wear blue jeans, white T-shirts, and sneakers. Much of the playing area is cluttered with props—mangled books, rolls of toilet paper, a huge doll, drums, an automobile tire, a ladder, a bicycle, two safari hats. LENA is seated at a small table at the rear of the stage area, taking notes. She has on black pants and a grey top and wears glasses. The young men continue to "fight." The camera moves in, and past the actors, until LENA occupies the center of the shot. She continues to write in a notebook. We now see, in the background of the shot, a very young woman in an advanced stage of pregnancy, talking earnestly on a wall telephone. She is LENA's ASSISTANT and glances frequently at LENA as she talks. LENA looks up and addresses the actors (who are not in the shot).

LENA

Take a break!

The pregnant woman leaves the phone, comes over to LENA, whispers in her ear.

LENA

I won't talk to him.

16

LENA's tone is firm, good-natured; she has the manner of some-one used to running things and doing it well. The pregnant woman seems inexperienced and insecure.

ASSISTANT
I'll tell him to call tomorrow.

Over the ASSISTANT's words we hear the sound of the actors scuf-fling again, then a thud as one of them hits the floor. LENA frowns good-humoredly.

LENA
No, you talk to him now. Tell him I'm going on vaca-tion.

LENA looks up sharply, hearing another loud noise.

LENA
(*To the actors*) Stop! (*To her* ASSISTANT) Listen, you can handle this. He really wants us to do his play. Coax him. He's just pretending to be indecisive.

The ASSISTANT reluctantly returns to the phone. Noise of more scuffling.

LENA laughs. She takes off her glasses and stands up. ▲

LENA
Stop being impossible, you two!

She crosses to the two young actors, puts an arm over the shoul-der of each.

LENA
I said improvise. Don't just have fun!

She slaps the boy on her left on the back, then turns away.

With mock solemnity they bow to each other. Then one attempts to climb on the other's shoulders.

Long shot of KAREN, who is on the narrow catwalk/balcony about twenty feet up which goes the whole circumference of the theatre. She is walking slowly from screen right to left, her left hand trailing along the surface of the railing; she looks down abstractedly at LENA and the two young men.

Wide high-angle shot (from KAREN's point of view) of LENA in the center of the stage area. She pivots, looks up, smiles and waves.

LENA

Karen! Just a minute!

A closer shot of KAREN, who seems ill at ease.

KAREN

I'll wait outside.

Both KAREN and LENA must shout, of course, to be heard over the music.

Back to wide high-angle shot (from KAREN's point of view) of LENA.

LENA

Stay there!

KAREN

(*Off*) How are you?

LENA

Fine!

She starts toward the back of the stage area.

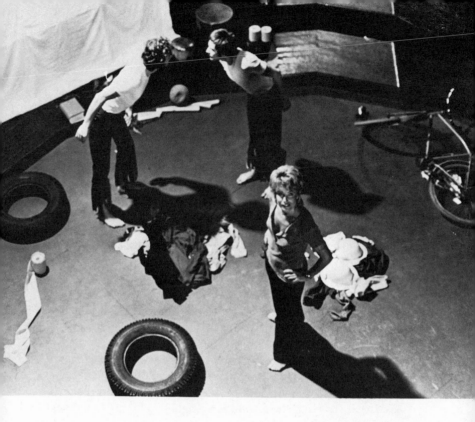

KAREN

(*Off*) Headache gone?

Wide shot of the catwalk/balcony (camera is on the opposite side): KAREN is waiting for LENA, obviously very upset. LENA enters the shot from the right, smiling warmly as she walks toward KAREN. She is slightly out of breath. As she continues toward KAREN, she surveys the cramped space.

LENA

(*With mock exasperation*) This is the only place around here where I can get some privacy . . . *What* headache?

LENA has reached KAREN now. The two women embrace affectionately.

KAREN

You said yesterday you were having a migraine.

LENA

Oh . . . (*Smiles.*) Who's being maternal now?

KAREN smiles shyly, with pleasure. LENA puts one arm around her and gives her a hug; she feels KAREN stiffen (though KAREN really does welcome LENA's demonstrativeness) and takes her arm away.

Leaning on the balustrade, LENA looks down at the two actors, who are continuing their exercises.

A high-angle shot of the two actors (from LENA's point of view). One is riding a bicycle; the other—mounted on his shoulders—holds a book from which he is declaiming. LENA's pregnant ASSISTANT is seated in the second row (right) watching them, next to a life-size doll.

Back to the two women. LENA is absorbed by what she sees down in the stage area; KAREN feels ignored.

KAREN

Listen, I'll come back.

LENA

No, you wait. I have time.

LENA's interest is still mainly held by the two actors clowning in the stage area below. She continues to look over the balustrade.

I complain about always having too much to do. But really I love it when it's like that.

It's as if she's talking to herself. She is smiling, amused by the actors' antics, savoring herself. Then she turns her head, really looks at KAREN for the first time, and becomes aware that KAREN is distraught. She straightens up.

LENA

What? You can't come with me.

KAREN averts her face.

KAREN

No! God, no! If you only knew how much I want to get away!

The last part of KAREN's line is partly covered by a loud crash, as if the two actors had fallen off the bicycle.

Medium shot of LENA.

> LENA
>
> Is it that bad?

Medium-close shot of KAREN.

> KAREN
>
> I'm bad.

> LENA
>
> (*Off*) That bad?

LENA's tone is tenderly mocking.

> KAREN
>
> I hate everyone. Peter. The child. My mother. You too . . . Am I supposed to say now that I hate myself too? I don't. I feel sorry for myself.

Wide shot of the two women, who face each other. LENA makes a slight movement, as if she wants to touch KAREN, then apparently changes her mind.

> KAREN
>
> Oh, Lena! If I were you, if I felt like you, if I could *do* things . . .

She looks down in the direction of the actors. Her voice gets quieter.

> KAREN
>
> I'm tired. She—

22

(*Pause*)
It takes a lot of energy to be able to love.

I'll give you some of mine.

The two women remain for a moment looking at each other, LENA smiling, KAREN frozen in her misery. Then KAREN smiles too; LENA's smile broadens; they begin to laugh together.

6. *Living room of Sandler apartment. Next morning*

One shot for the whole sequence. On the right, PETER, wearing a dark business suit, is checking his partly open briefcase to see that he has all his papers—or perhaps just mechanically fumbling with it to stall for time. KAREN is sitting on a cabinet or low table next to the window, her back against the wall, her legs crossed; she is wearing a white terry-cloth bathrobe and has a white towel wrapped around her head. On the left side of the frame, ANNA stands on the recessed ledge of the window. She is wearing only a pair of underpants, as in sequence 1. Her back is against the window, and with her right hand she is pounding slowly and irregularly on the windowpane. ANNA is staring straight ahead, as usual—and gives no sign of noticing what her parents are doing. KAREN glances at ANNA, then turns away. PETER, worried, closes his briefcase. He stands in front of KAREN.

PETER
How long will you be gone?

KAREN answers in a dull voice.

23

KAREN

I don't know.

PETER

A week?

KAREN

Maybe two.

ANNA continues knocking on the windowpane, not looking at her parents. PETER stands there indecisively. KAREN turns her head in ANNA's direction. She speaks in a tone of weary sarcasm.

KAREN

If you don't leave right now, that fascinating client of yours will already have gotten himself a new lawyer.

PETER

Suppose I insist that you don't go.

KAREN turns back toward PETER.

KAREN

(*Softly*) Don't insist.

PETER leans toward KAREN. Their faces come together.

PETER

But you are . . . coming back?

KAREN

Don't ask.

After another moment, PETER straightens up and leaves the image (screen left). Impassive, KAREN settles back in her position, watching ANNA. The child continues knocking.

24

Music ('Anna theme') throughout sequence, plus natural sounds.
City noises (cars, etc.) up loud at the end, after PETER leaves.

7. Pier (Saltsjöbaden). A day later: morning

Very long shot, from the pier, of the gangplank being thrown
down as the ferryboat finishes docking. Sharp sound of the
gangplank hitting the pier; voices of passengers, small boats,
the sea, birds. People (vacationers, tourists) start coming off
the boat. Bright sunshine.

Closer shot, high angle (the camera is on the boat), of the passengers disembarking. They move from screen right to screen left. We see KAREN and LENA. KAREN wears a white turtleneck sweater, blue denim jacket. LENA wears a white raincoat and glasses.

Very long shot, taken from the pier. KAREN and LENA come down the gangplank, toward the camera. KAREN carries a medium-size suitcase and a canvas carry-all hanging at her side from a shoulder strap; LENA has a smallish suitcase, a typewriter, and a shoulder bag. People waiting on the pier to meet people coming off the boat, all wearing casual clothes except for one blond man, standing to the left of the gangplank, who wears white tie and tails; he looks anxiously at each passenger who comes off the boat. KAREN and LENA are among the last to disembark.

8. Bridge, pavilion (Saltsjöbaden). Moments later

▼ Very long shot. KAREN first—with LENA behind her—is walking over the small bridge, from screen left to screen right.

LENA

I wired him, but I knew he wouldn't come to meet us.

Long shot of the pavilion, which is enclosed by a wall about four feet high (bottom half, whitewashed wood; top half, glass). It has a dozen metal tables with chairs. The camera is inside. Only two tables are occupied, of those shown: at a table mid-ground are two old ladies, both wearing similar wide-brimmed hats. They are talking. Farther back in the shot, sitting alone at a table alongside the partition, is MARTIN. He is
▲ reading a newspaper.

Medium shot of MARTIN at the table. The camera is outside

the pavilion; that is, he is seen through the glass. He reads a moment longer, then looks up (he has seen LENA and KAREN approaching), puts down the newspaper. (The two women are not yet in the shot.) He sits waiting, his face impassive. He is in his early forties; his build is stocky; he has a short beard, neatly trimmed, but his hair is longish and unkempt. He wears a heavy sweater, unpressed khaki pants, and hiking boots.

The camera starts pulling back just as MARTIN stands up. LENA and KAREN come into the shot, from the left. LENA is smiling. She puts down her suitcase and typewriter.

LENA
Were you pretending not to see us?

MARTIN leans over the top of the partition and puts his arms around LENA. They kiss lightly but their eyes linger. KAREN, not yet acknowledged by MARTIN, is standing behind LENA in the foreground of the image, with her back to the camera; embarrassed by what she imagines LENA is feeling, she turns her head away (to the left) and down. Then MARTIN turns to KAREN, smiles politely, and extends his hand.

MARTIN
(To KAREN) It's been a long time.

KAREN nods. MARTIN turns back to LENA, who is gazing at him, her face radiant. He climbs on the table and sits on the top of the partition, looking down at them, with a distracted or perplexed air. As if seeking to make conversation, he turns to LENA to ask a question.

MARTIN
Did you get a room? I hear the hotel is crowded.

LENA
(Smiling) Yes.

MARTIN

Are you tired?

LENA

Of course not.

Sound of boat leaving harbor. MARTIN hesitates a second longer, then jumps down (on their side of the partition).

MARTIN

Okay. Let's drop your things.

He picks up LENA's suitcase and holds out his hand to take KAREN's. (She has never put hers down.)

MARTIN

(*To* KAREN) May I?

KAREN nods, a little flustered, and hands MARTIN her suitcase. Carrying the two suitcases, MARTIN sets out down the long straight path (away from the camera) which leads toward the hotel. MARTIN walks ahead of the women. He speaks without turning his head.

MARTIN

I suppose you want to see my new place.

The camera is behind all three. KAREN drops behind LENA. At MARTIN's words, LENA glances swiftly at KAREN (screen left).

9. *Veranda, front room of Martin's cottage* (*in the woods near Saltsjöbaden*). *Shortly after*

Full shot of glass doors to MARTIN's cottage. Through the doors we can see the sparsely furnished front room. The sound of footsteps. The reflections of MARTIN, LENA, and KAREN in the glass. MARTIN, who is in the lead, pushes the door open.

Full shot of the three. The camera, at the back of the room, is facing the door. They have just entered. KAREN remains by the door. (She has taken off her denim jacket and has it slung over her shoulder.) Tossing her bag on the striped couch on the left side of the room, LENA walks toward the camera. Her look is curious, boldly appraising. MARTIN leaves the shot on the left.

Reverse shot (camera is by the front door). At the back of the room is the doorway to MARTIN's sleeping room; there is no door. We see a plain double bed and a bookshelf above it. (MARTIN's one-story cottage, which was built in the eighteenth century, has four rooms, square in shape, that connect with each other by doorways that lack a door. Each room has a fire-place; the four fireplaces feed into a common chimney.)

LENA advances to the threshold of the sleeping room, holds the frame of the doorway with both hands, leans in, then turns around to face MARTIN (who is off-screen).

> LENA
> A little glad to see us? Tell the truth.

Medium shot, from another angle, of MARTIN, standing in the center of the front room. Bending over, he is taking off one boot. He rubs his foot, shakes out his boot. Two pebbles fall out. He puts the boot back on and laces it up awkwardly, hob-bling on one foot. It's in the middle of this that he delivers his line, barely looking in LENA's direction. (She is off-screen.)

> MARTIN
> Give me time to see how I like it.

The camera pans, eliminating MARTIN to show LENA. She is seated on the striped couch; on the far side of the couch is a fireplace stacked with fresh logs and kindling.

LENA

(*Bitterly*) I forgot how slow you'd become.

During LENA's line, MARTIN enters the shot from the right, kneels, lights a match, and starts a fire. LENA looks down at him. He is ignoring the two women.

LENA

Talk to us.

MARTIN continues busying himself with the fire for a few seconds more, then rises. As he stands, the camera tilts up, eliminating LENA from the shot. MARTIN's face and upper body are

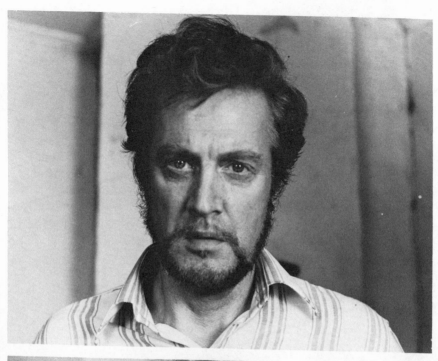

in the center of the frame. He is perspiring. He crosses his arms to grasp the bottom of his sweater, speaking at the same moment as he makes the upward movement to pull off the sweater. (He is wearing a striped shirt underneath.)

Us?

MARTIN throws the sweater across the room, aiming at a wooden peg to the right of the front door (off-screen). It is clear from his expression that he misses. He crosses the room—the camera pans with him—to pick up the sweater from the floor and hang it up on the peg. The camera stops when KAREN, still standing by the open front door, is included in the shot. She looks blank, impassive. MARTIN turns around to face LENA.

Reverse angle: medium shot of LENA, standing in the threshold between the front room and the sleeping room. She looks at MARTIN (i.e., at the camera), accepting the challenge.

LENA

All right. *Me.*

Back to shot (from LENA's point of view) of MARTIN. He is standing quite near KAREN, but without acknowledging her presence. KAREN looks anxiously at MARTIN and at LENA (off-screen). MARTIN's tone is icy.

MARTIN

You chose to come here. I didn't ask you.

KAREN, flinching at MARTIN's words, bows her head with impotent sympathy for LENA.

Medium close-up of LENA. Her face seems to darken, as defiance and hope give way to the bitter fear of defeat. Sound of steps. (It is KAREN leaving.) Music starts. LENA's face continues to change.

10. *Outside Martin's cottage. Seconds later*

Very wide shot. The camera, facing the cottage, pans with KAREN as she hurries across the veranda, down the steps, and onto the path that begins in front of the cottage. Her jacket is still slung over one shoulder.

Very long shot. KAREN is running down the path, into the woods, toward the sea. The camera pans with her—she moves from screen left to screen right—with a telescopic lens; she is partly obscured by the trees. Gradually she outdistances the camera, and goes out of the shot to the right.

Music that starts at the end of sequence 9 continues throughout sequence 10, with the sound of the sea becoming audible at the end.

11. *Rocky shore. Minutes later*

Very long shot: woods in the foreground, the sea in the background. We see KAREN approaching, still running. She comes out of the wooded area (toward the camera), slows down, then stops. She is standing on a stretch of flat boulders about fifteen feet above the water.

Long shot of CARL, standing on a rock at the water's edge. He is raising a metal fishing net out of the sea. His movements are slow, trance-like. He wears a loose shirt and trousers rolled up to his mid-calves; he is barefoot. This is the same shot as sequence 3.*

Closer shot of CARL. He raises the net higher.

---

* Sequence 3 was cut in the final version of the film.

Back to KAREN, watching CARL intently. She is cold and starts to put on her jacket.

Close shot of the large, gleaming net which CARL is slowly lowering into the water. It is empty. Splash of the net as it hits the water.

Another shot of KAREN. In a slowed-down movement that, consciously or unconsciously, mimics the rhythm of CARL's activity, she finishes putting on her jacket—never taking her eyes off CARL. Then, abruptly, she turns to leave.

Note: KAREN and CARL never appear in the same shot in this sequence, but the distance between them, about thirty feet, should be clear. Whatever the difference of visual values in the shots, CARL is always shown on the same axis—from KAREN's point of view; that is, from behind. He, of course, remains unaware of KAREN's presence.

Natural sounds—sea, wind—as well as music throughout (continuation of music in sequences 9 and 10).

12. *Front room of Martin's cottage. A half-hour later*

Medium two-shot: MARTIN, in the foreground and in profile, is in a chair, has his arms around LENA, seen frontally; she is to his right, kneeling, her arms around him and her head on his chest. MARTIN seems half asleep. LENA's expression is tender,

self-confident. (The audience shouldn't realize in this shot that we are back in MARTIN's cottage.) They remain in this position a few moments. Then LENA looks up.

> LENA
> You shouldn't let yourself put on so much weight.

MARTIN makes a small, weary noise of assent. LENA smiles—dotingly, seductively.

> LENA
> You don't get enough exercise any more.

She disengages herself from his embrace, takes his right hand, and tries to pull him out of the chair and onto the floor with her. He resists for a moment, then follows her.

Change to a wider shot, as MARTIN follows LENA down to the floor. She is lying on her right side. He lowers himself down slowly, letting his head come to rest in her lap. He closes his eyes. LENA, leaning on her right elbow, caresses MARTIN's hair with her left hand.

> LENA
> It's matted.

With her left hand LENA takes a comb out of her pocket and starts gently combing his hair. MARTIN opens his eyes and looks up (off-screen, in the direction of the camera). LENA's attention is completely directed to MARTIN; her head is behind and above his.

> MARTIN
> Are we making you uncomfortable?

Full shot of KAREN, standing in the same place by the door as in sequence 9, watching them (looking out of the frame); it is

36

to her that MARTIN's first words in this sequence are addressed.
At the change of shot, the audience should be surprised that
KAREN is there again.

KAREN

No.

KAREN is immobile; the expression on her face is benevolent, de-
tached.

MARTIN

(*Off*) Embarrassed?

No.

High angle two-shot, from KAREN's point of view, of MARTIN and LENA on the floor. MARTIN lies stretched out, his head in LENA's lap. LENA, half sitting behind him, passes the comb through his hair, then caresses it. She does not once look at KAREN. MARTIN is still gazing up at KAREN.

MARTIN

Perhaps you're moved. Do we seem pathetic?
(*Pause*)
Maybe we're exciting you sexually.

Back to KAREN, closer shot. Her ironic air breaks. Evidently distressed, she shakes her head and turns away for a moment; then she looks back at them.

Medium shot of LENA and MARTIN. She glances up for a second in KAREN's direction, then passes the comb roughly through MARTIN's hair. He grimaces.

MARTIN

That's enough!

He sits up abruptly. LENA, moving to a sitting position (on her heels), refuses to acknowledge MARTIN's change of mood. She touches his hair again.

LENA

Where are the scissors?

MARTIN

No.

MARTIN runs his fingers through his hair, making it messy again. As he quickly gets to his feet, the camera dollies back fast to

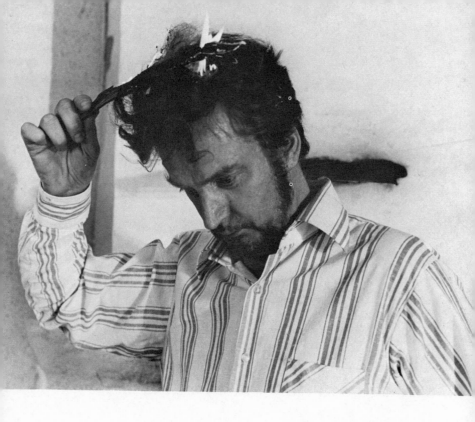

show him in full shot, then moves in closer again to follow him as he goes to the fireplace. (LENA is now out of the shot.) MARTIN bends over, pulls out a small burning stick, straightens up and pivots (to face LENA), raises the stick to his head, and sets fire to his hair.

LENA

(*Off*) No!

MARTIN calmly lets his hair burn for several seconds, then puts out the flame by slapping his head with his left hand. Then he reaches out to LENA and with both hands pulls her up to a standing position beside him.

39

Change of shot: what we have now is a medium shot of LENA and MARTIN, both seen in profile, facing each other (LENA screen left, MARTIN screen right). KAREN is in the background, slightly out of focus, still at the door, watching them. LENA stares at MARTIN bitterly for a moment before she speaks.

                              LENA
        It's a contest then.

                              MARTIN
        I hope not.

                              LENA
        Why? Because one of us has to lose?

MARTIN walks past LENA to the left side of the room (i.e., he leaves the shot on the left). Turning to look at him, LENA now occupies the center foreground of the shot; KAREN remains in the background, not moving.

LENA

Do you know why I'm here?

Three-quarter shot (from LENA's point of view) of MARTIN standing at the window, his back to the camera. There is an open field outside; the sun is shining brightly.

MARTIN

Yes.

LENA

(Off) And your answer?

MARTIN

No.

The image holds on MARTIN's immobile figure for another moment.

13. *Hotel room, balcony (Grand Hotel, Saltsjöbaden). That evening*

Medium close-up of LENA, somberly lit. She is pacing back and forth. (As we will see subsequently, she is wearing a white shirt which just covers her white underpants; she is barelegged and barefoot.) The camera moves with her; perhaps it loses her for a moment (or gets ahead) and then catches up with her (or waits for her to catch up). LENA's first line has already begun (as a voice 'off,' with a slight echo effect) over the end of the last shot of the preceding sequence.

LENA

I'm *not* humiliating myself! I'm just asking for what I want.

She glances at someone off-screen. (The audience, having no clue during this shot as to where LENA is, should at first assume that she is talking to MARTIN.)

LENA

I know *you'd* never do what I'm doing. That's why you don't understand.

She stops pacing. Her expression softens.

LENA

You know, he misses me a lot. It's funny, but true.

(Now, of course, the audience will realize she is not talking to MARTIN.) She turns again.

▼ LENA goes out through the open French doors onto the balcony (screen right). The camera holds back a little, showing her now in medium shot, from the back.

Full still shot—the camera is on the balcony now—of LENA at the edge of the balcony, looking out into the night. (The hotel room is on the second floor and faces the water.) Sound of motorboats. We vaguely see nearby trees (on the hotel grounds) and lights (of boats, houses) in the distance.

KAREN

(*Off*) Lena!

LENA remains on the balcony a moment longer, then returns to the room. The camera follows behind. Now we see the hotel room for the first time. It is furnished in an eclectic style: pat-

42

terned wallpaper, an ornate dresser, a Chinese vase with flowers, a small roll-top desk, a cane rocking chair, heavy curtains on the windows, an ugly floral tapestry on the far wall. There are open suitcases on two chairs.

LENA is in three-quarter shot, from behind. She crosses the room (moving away from the balcony).

LENA
He's not really strong. People think he's a monster of egotism. That goes with his . . . profession, I suppose.

Wide shot: KAREN. At the rear of the room is an alcove with twin beds. On the night table between the two beds is a lamp and two books; above the beds hang a pair of old-fashioned oval portraits, one of a woman and the other of a man, in a rectangular frame. KAREN is sitting up in the bed to the left. She wears a white nightgown and is partly under the covers.

KAREN
How can you fight any harder than you already have?

Full shot of LENA. Having crossed the room, LENA turns left into the passageway beyond the alcove. This passageway, which leads to the bathroom, is created by a partition of wooden slats which extends along the far side of the sleeping area parallel to the far wall. LENA stops.

LENA
But I *didn't* fight then.
(*Pause*)
I have to feel strong to fight. I have to exist.

Medium shot of KAREN, in bed. She does not look at LENA.

Three-quarters frontal shot of LENA on the other side of the partition (KAREN's point of view). LENA is looking through the slats at KAREN.

LENA

At first it was Martin who seemed to have all the doubts
. . . Especially about his work. And I wasn't very re-
assuring, I suppose. That kind of theatre had always
seemed to me just . . . beautiful. Too beautiful.

(*Pause*)

Then I heard ugly rumors about him and a girl in the
company. People even dragged in stories—about Carl
Norén.

Shot of KAREN in bed, listening. She shifts her position.

Back to LENA, same shot—through the slatted partition (KAREN's
point of view).

LENA

When I asked Martin, he wouldn't deny them.

LENA seems to be talking half to herself, half to KAREN.

LENA

It got worse. The times he seemed helpless, I became
afraid. Still, I felt strong because—even then—he acknowledged me. But sometimes . . . a look came into
his eyes that—without any cruelty—simply . . . annihi-
lated me.

Medium shot of KAREN.

KAREN

You annihilate each other. I don't like watching it!

She draws the covers back around her. Sound of steps. (Off-
screen, LENA has entered the bathroom.)

LENA

(*Off*) Then go back to town.

▼

44

KAREN

I don't *want* to go back to town.

▲

Wide shot, which is divided in half—vertically—by the slatted partition. In the rear of the shot, on the right half, we see LENA through the open door of the bathroom. She is in profile, facing right: standing at the sink, running the faucet. Sound of water. KAREN is in the left half of the image, in bed, facing the camera. KAREN abruptly sits up in bed and hugs her knees. The water sound ceases. LENA comes out of the bathroom, down the passageway (toward the camera). She holds a glass of water and some pills, which she swallows before getting within KAREN's view. Her walk is unsteady. Reaching the end of the passageway, she pauses briefly. Leaning against the partition and not looking at KAREN, she speaks in a tone of almost convincing self-confidence.

LENA

I think he's going to ask me to stay.

She comes around the partition (screen left) and approaches her bed—the one next to the partition—as KAREN watches her sadly.

KAREN

Do you?

LENA puts the glass on the night table between the two beds, and throws herself, face up, on her bed.

Close shot of KAREN, who leans forward on her left elbow toward LENA. Her tone is gentle.

KAREN

Lena?

Close-up of LENA's face on the pillow. She doesn't answer. She is breathing heavily, and looks as if she is trying not to cry.

45

14. *Hotel room. Early next morning*

Medium shot of KAREN; the camera is behind her. She stands before the window in strong sunlight; we see, out the window, the hotel garden and the jetty that belongs to the hotel. Boats in the distance. With a sharp movement KAREN pulls the heavy curtains together; the light drops.

> KAREN'S VOICE
> To act without hope.

She is wearing matching dark grey jersey pants and a sleeveless vest, a striped blouse, and a silk scarf inside the long open collar of the blouse.

Full shot, reverse angle. KAREN crosses the room, walking toward the sleeping alcove. We see LENA still asleep; she wears a black eye mask. KAREN pauses for a second at the foot of LENA's bed.

> KAREN'S VOICE
> To speak without an echo.

She moves away from the bed, screen left, and turns into the corridor that leads toward the door of the room. LENA opens her eyes.

> KAREN'S VOICE
> Not to dream of saving anyone. Not to long to be saved.

LENA stares blankly, without turning her head in the direction we have seen KAREN go.

Medium shot: KAREN at the door. She puts her hand on the knob, hesitates, glances back once, then stands there without moving. Quick fade. Blackness for several seconds, during which time we hear the door opening.

46

15. *Outside Martin's cottage. An hour later*

Wide shot: MARTIN and KAREN. MARTIN is two or three rungs up a ladder that is leaning against the side of the cottage. He is looking down at KAREN, who is standing on the ground next to the ladder (nearer the camera). MARTIN wears a heavy brown wool sweater, white jeans, and boots. KAREN is dressed as in the previous sequence.

> MARTIN
> You didn't just wander by here accidentally.
> (*Pause*)
> You want to talk about Lena.
> (*Pause*)
> But I'm a difficult person to talk to, don't you know that?

He takes one more step up the ladder.

> MARTIN
> Everybody knows that. Even Lena.

On these words, MARTIN continues up to the top of the ladder (out of the image). KAREN moves so that she now stands at the foot of the ladder looking up at him.

Wide shot, very low angle, from KAREN's point of view, of MARTIN standing on the edge of the roof. Behind him, a cloud is moving in the bright sky. He extends his arms and raises one leg.

> MARTIN
> Did you know I can fly?

He makes a movement as if to jump.

Medium shot of KAREN, looking up, clutching the ladder and visibly frightened.

Come down!

Wide shot, low angle, showing both MARTIN and KAREN. MARTIN, still in 'flying position' at the roof's edge, looks down at KAREN for another moment, then relaxes and sits down at the top of the ladder. His tone is rueful, self-mocking.

MARTIN
I used to think I could fly.

He starts down the ladder.

MARTIN
Everybody does. It's so stupid!

New shot, taken from inside the front room. Through the window, we see MARTIN reach the bottom of the ladder. He takes KAREN's arm. They go out of the shot to the right.

Wide shot; camera is on the far side of the cottage. KAREN and MARTIN, he still holding her by the arm, come around the corner (moving toward the camera).

MARTIN
Do you realize how many people there are in the world who go on believing they can fly?
(*Pause*)
Or make everyone good?
(*Pause*)
Or raise the dead?

By MARTIN's third line, they have crossed the front of the house and start up the veranda steps.

Each of MARTIN's last three lines is strongly punctuated by music ('miracle theme'). Between ". . . believing they can

48

fly?" and "Or make everyone good?" one or two measures; after "Or raise the dead?" a long dissonant chord.

Besides the music, which comes in only at the sequence's end, we hear natural sounds—somewhat exaggerated—such as wind, footsteps, etc., throughout.

16. *Front room and sleeping room of Martin's cottage. Minutes later*

Medium close-up of MARTIN's face.

> MARTIN
> (*Fiercely*) I told you, I'm no good at giving people what they want.

He pauses, waiting for an answer from KAREN (off-screen), but there is no word from her.

> MARTIN
> You think I'm cruel, don't you?

> KAREN
> (*Off*) Yes.

Wide two-shot of MARTIN and KAREN, both seen frontally, with MARTIN in the foreground. They are seated on two sides of a low square unpainted table on the right side of the front room. There are two beer cans, an atlas, two candlesticks, and a recorder on the table. KAREN gets up and, passing in front of MARTIN (between MARTIN and the camera, her torso blocking him for a moment), moves around the table to the wall. Propped against the wall is a large blowup of a photograph of twins *in utero*. MARTIN still keeps his back to KAREN. Standing behind him, KAREN touches the photograph with an absent air;

49

the tip of her left index finger traces the outline of the right ear of the twin whose head is upright.

> MARTIN
>
> Maybe. But I'm much less . . . cruel . . . than I used to be.

KAREN looks at him, then sits down.

> MARTIN
>
> (*As if to himself*) Yes.

New shot (camera is behind KAREN). As if suddenly aware again of KAREN's existence, MARTIN turns and leans toward her, holding out his hand.

MARTIN

Come.

MARTIN takes KAREN's hand and stands up. Reluctantly, she
stands too and, stepping over the table, follows him. MARTIN
leads KAREN toward the sleeping room—the room just behind
the front room.

Change of shot. The camera is now inside the sleeping room.
MARTIN and KAREN enter the room, MARTIN preceding KAREN,
still holding her by the hand. MARTIN sits down at the foot of
the double bed (covered with a plain white spread) and releases
KAREN's hand. KAREN stands, facing him.

KAREN

You're making fun of me. You're making fun of us both.

MARTIN

Don't you believe I want you?

KAREN

I think you don't want anything.

MARTIN

(*Ironic*) You see, you do understand me—already . . .

MARTIN takes KAREN by her belt and draws her down on the
bed alongside him.

MARTIN

Now you know why I left Lena five years ago.

New shot, from the side of the bed. KAREN is in the foreground.
She is tilted backward on the bed, supporting herself on her
elbows. MARTIN (behind her in the shot) lies on his right side,
propped up on his right elbow. He looks closely at KAREN. In
the rear of the shot (against the wall, to the left of the one

window in the room) is a large blowup of a photograph of a woman (her head and shoulders), wide-eyed, doll-like.

MARTIN

Why are you here on the bed with me?

KAREN doesn't reply, doesn't look at him. MARTIN leans toward her, undoes her scarf, and kisses her neck lightly. KAREN remains entirely passive. Only when MARTIN has moved his head away from hers does she speak.

KAREN

Don't play these games with Lena. Please!

MARTIN

Out of pity?

KAREN

If that's the only reason you have—yes.

MARTIN

Would you do it for that reason?

As she answers, KAREN stands up, crosses to the window, and ties her scarf again.

KAREN

Oh, *I'm* no standard . . .

She turns back from the window, passes along the wall—the camera pans with her—and stops to the left of the doorway. Hanging on the wall, screen left of her head, is a crude Sicilian ex-voto painted on wood, depicting an accident (a little boy being hit by a car). She stares with cool detachment at MARTIN (who is off-camera). Then, on a sound—like someone falling over a metal garbage pail—coming from outside the cottage, she turns sharply.

Off-camera, MARTIN has gotten up. He enters the shot at the doorway and pauses for a moment beside KAREN, without looking at her or touching her. Then he continues into the front room. Through the doorway, we see him place himself on the small striped couch (next to the wall on the right) so that his legs are straight up against the wall and his head hangs down toward the floor. He shuts his eyes. In the background of the shot, propped against the far wall to the right of the front door, is a large blowup of a photograph of a woman's head and neck (in left profile): an anatomical model, with the skin of the neck pulled back, exposing the network of muscles, veins, and arteries.

Reverse angle shot (the camera is low, on the far side of the couch), showing MARTIN's head in the foreground and in the rear right of the shot KAREN (in full figure) standing in the doorway, looking down at MARTIN. She is surprised, angry.

KAREN
Is that the way you dismiss people?

She pauses another moment, then enters the front room. As she passes in front of MARTIN, he speaks (still not opening his eyes). His voice is flat.

MARTIN
Excuse me for not walking you back to the hotel.

KAREN goes out of the shot (toward the front door). We hear the sound of the door opening, steps. MARTIN remains in the same upside-down position. Then we hear a muffled cry (KAREN, off) coming from outside. MARTIN turns his head sharply, opens his eyes wide. Fast cut.

17. *Near Martin's cottage. A moment later*

Medium shot of KAREN and CARL, struggling. KAREN is whimpering with fear. CARL has seized KAREN's arms and won't let go; CARL's outstretched arms are rigid; his eyes stare fixedly and his face is expressionless. He is wearing loose white and grey striped pajamas and is barefoot.

Full shot. KAREN and CARL are in the foreground of the shot; MARTIN's cottage is in the background. (KAREN and CARL are about ten yards from the house.) We see MARTIN running on the veranda, down the steps, and toward them. KAREN and CARL (she still locked in his rigid grip, struggling to free herself) move out of the shot on the right side. The camera pans to pick them up again. MARTIN enters the shot from the left and pulls them apart. CARL backs off, goes out of the shot. MARTIN puts his arms around KAREN and holds her; she is gasping with fear. He looks in CARL's direction (off-screen) then back at KAREN.

> MARTIN
> I'm sorry! I didn't know he was up.

Full frontal shot of CARL, who slowly retreats, walking backward. He looks dazed.

Another shot of KAREN and MARTIN. He has one arm around her.

> MARTIN
> Don't be afraid. He won't hurt you.

> KAREN
> He didn't say a word!

Wider shot, showing all three. MARTIN turns toward CARL and holds out his hand.

MARTIN

(*Gently*) It's a friend, Carl.

CARL, standing about fifteen feet from MARTIN and KAREN, shakes his head violently (once).

KAREN

I've seen him before!

MARTIN

Of course you have. Everyone has.

KAREN

(*Puzzled*) I saw him yesterday—

MARTIN interrupts.

MARTIN

Karen, it's Carl Norén. Don't you recognize him? Didn't you ever see him dance?

KAREN gazes at CARL.

KAREN

(*Slowly*) Of course . . . Years and years ago . . . But it can't be! He's too young.

Full shot of CARL. He walks, stiff-gaited, away from MARTIN and KAREN, down a slope, at the foot of which is a tree. (He is now about eight yards from them.)

MARTIN

(*Off*) Maybe the absence of . . . a life . . . all these years keeps Carl looking young.

CARL reaches out and touches the bark of the tree.

MARTIN

(*Off*) Sometimes he gets better. But it never lasts.

CARL starts to move behind the tree.

Close frontal shot of CARL, hiding: he is peering at MARTIN and
KAREN through a fork in the tree, his face partly covered by
leaves.

MARTIN

(*Off*) He doesn't often want to come and stay with
me. It's already longer than usual this time. A month.

A deep-focus shot showing MARTIN and KAREN, both facing
forward. KAREN is in the foreground, gazing fixedly at CARL
(off-screen, right); MARTIN is behind her.

He prefers to sleep up there.

He motions with his hand to a tiny one-room cabin, half buried in the ground—it is an old earth cellar—about twenty-five yards behind him (not far from the cottage) that is visible in the rear of the shot.

Full shot of CARL. He comes out from behind the tree, and stiffly walks up the short slope toward MARTIN and KAREN. He looks at the ground as he walks. When he reaches level ground, he stops, and remains in a rigid position.

Two-shot of MARTIN and KAREN. KAREN, a stricken look on her face, advances slowly toward CARL (off-screen, right). MARTIN remains where he is (behind KAREN), watching. KAREN extends her hand.

KAREN
Hello, Carl.

Medium shot of CARL. He stares at her without making any move.

Back to two-shot. KAREN turns her head to MARTIN, to look for a clue, then turns back to face CARL, more and more appalled. (Cut in flash shot: medium close-up of ANNA. Almost subliminal.)

Reverse angle: medium shot of CARL. He casts a shrewd, compassionate look at KAREN—then drops his eyes.

Back to two-shot of MARTIN and KAREN, KAREN in foreground.

Flash shot: medium close-up of ANNA. (Several frames more than previous flash shot.)

Back to CARL, looking at KAREN as if he has seen what she sees.

Back to two-shot of MARTIN and KAREN. She is transfixed.

MARTIN

Go on.

MARTIN's words break the spell. KAREN turns convulsively to
face him.

KAREN

I can't. It reminds me—

MARTIN attempts to put his arms around KAREN.

58

MARTIN

I'm sorry! I'd forgotten . . . But Carl isn't like your—

KAREN, close to tears, breaks away from MARTIN's embrace.

KAREN

I must go!

KAREN runs in the direction of the cottage (away from the camera), moving from the center foreground to the left rear of the shot. At the cut, she is just passing the left side of the cottage.

Three-quarter shot of CARL, still maintaining the same frozen pose. He follows her with his eyes.

18. Pavilion near hotel. Same day, almost noon

Camera is just outside the pavilion (already seen in sequence 8), tracking from right to left along the partition; there are reflections of boats in the glass. It tracks past several empty tables along the inside of the partition to pick up a table occupied on one side (screen right) by a blond woman around thirty with a large scar on her left cheek, and on the other side (screen left) by twin boys around ten years old. The woman wears a short-sleeve polka-dot dress; the boys wear identical white shirts, dark shorts, high white socks, and sandals. The camera stays on them a few moments. The children are very restless: giggling, moving around their plates, shifting noisily in their chairs. Their mother reaches across the table to try to quiet them (she doesn't say anything).

The camera continues tracking leftward until it picks up the table, set somewhat back from the partition, where LENA and KAREN sit. (All other tables in the pavilion shown during this sequence are unoccupied.)

Medium long shot of LENA and KAREN—the camera is inside the
pavilion now—facing each other; the camera is nearer KAREN.
They are finishing breakfast. LENA is wearing matching beige
knit pants and a short-sleeve top. KAREN is dressed as in sequences 14, 15, 16, and 17. An exit from the pavilion is just
beyond their table (behind LENA's chair).

                    LENA
    It never *occurred* to me Martin might have him here
    now.

KAREN puts some sugar in her coffee. Noise of the twins in
background.

                    KAREN
▼   But Lena! It's Carl Norén . . .

LENA

The great Carl Norén has very little to do with the lunatic who attacked you this morning.

▲

LENA

You're sure he didn't hurt you?

KAREN

No! I must have frightened him.

Noise of the twins, up.

Long shot of the other table (from the point of view of LENA and KAREN). Shrieking, the twins shove against each other, noisily push back their metal chairs and stand, then try to pull their mother out of hers. She resists, laughing. (Again, no words are spoken.) They give up, and run out of the shot—screen right—in the direction of LENA and KAREN. The mother remains at the table. She puts her face in her hands and starts counting, loudly, very slowly.

MOTHER

One . . . two . . . three . . .

Back to two-shot of KAREN and LENA at their table. The camera is nearer LENA, who seems to let go of an emotion. She twists the ring on her finger.

LENA

I guess I don't have very kindly feelings about Carl Norén.
(Pause)
Sometimes I feel as if he—oh, it's an old story!

In these last words, LENA gives the impression that she is about to confide in KAREN, but suddenly changes her mind. (During LENA's line, the TWINS' MOTHER—off-camera—continues to be heard faintly: "Four . . . five . . . six . . . seven . . .")

Back to the shot of the TWINS' MOTHER, still with her face in her hands.

> MOTHER
> Eight . . . nine . . . ten!

She looks up.

Back to shot of LENA and KAREN. Background sound of the twins squealing. KAREN leans back in her chair.

> KAREN
> Lena, I don't think he's dangerous . . .

Long shot of a hillock just outside the pavilion. The twins are ▼
hiding behind some rocks at the top; the heads bob up and
down. They are giggling.

KAREN

(*Off*) How easy life would be if all the dangerous people
behaved like madmen. But they don't, you know.

LENA

(*Off*) You're warning me against Martin.

KAREN

(*Off*) Yes.   ▲

Another medium long shot of the two women. KAREN leans
forward in her chair.

KAREN

When I went there this morning, he . . . Be careful,
Lena. He's stronger than you are.

LENA takes a sip of coffee, then bursts out.

LENA

Stronger! How can anyone be stronger who can barely
endure being alive . . . At least I can make myself
happy working. These last years Martin can't even do
that.

KAREN

You need to think he's weak. But—

There is a sudden crash. The twins have just reentered the
pavilion area, and one of them, chased by the other, has col-
lided with the table. LENA is still holding the coffee cup; the
jolt makes some coffee spill on her lap. Hardly breaking their
stride, laughing hysterically, the boys scamper away (out of the

shot, left). The camera pulls back as KAREN half rises to assist LENA.

KAREN

Oh!

KAREN pulls a handkerchief out of her pocket.

LENA

(*Harshly*) Don't! I'm all right.

LENA looks very upset. She jabs at the stain on her clothes with a napkin. KAREN tries to reach her with the handkerchief.

KAREN

Let me help.

LENA

No!

LENA rises with a violent movement and turns to leave the pavilion. (The exit is just behind her chair.) She puts her right hand against the side of the gate, and looks back at KAREN, a look that forbids KAREN to follow her.

LENA

(*Coldly*) I have to change.

KAREN stands up.

KAREN

I'll come with you.

LENA, without replying, turns and walks out of the pavilion (away from the camera).

Full shot of LENA. The camera tracks alongside LENA as she walks rapidly along the waterfront path that leads from the

pavilion to the hotel. A moment later KAREN catches up with
her (entering the shot). LENA speaks without looking at KAREN.

LENA

Martin is fascinating, isn't he?

KAREN

Stop it, Lena! I'm coming to be with *you*.

There is great warmth in KAREN's voice, but LENA, not to be
won over at this moment, answers her sarcastically.

LENA

Sure it's safe for you to give way to these late-blooming
maternal impulses?

KAREN stops walking, hurt by LENA's remark. But what prevails
is her sympathy for LENA's distress. Without turning, LENA
stops too.

Full shot. The camera is in front of the two women. Now
KAREN stands behind and slightly to the right of LENA. She puts
one hand on LENA's shoulder. LENA stares stonily ahead.

KAREN

Let me.

LENA's face suddenly looks bewildered and sad. LENA covers
with her own the hand which KAREN rests on her shoulder.

LENA

All right. Come.

▲

19. Beach. The next day: afternoon

Very wide shot. A warm day, with bright sun; the sea. In the rear of the shot, we see CARL walking along the curved shoreline (moving in the direction of the camera); his gait is noticeably uneven. As he walks he scans the ground, and occasionally stoops to pick up what he sees—a wooden crate, a woman's stocking, a rag doll, a rock—throwing everything back on the ground after examining it, except one rock that he pockets. CARL wears a khaki safari jacket with deep pockets, and the bottoms of his loose striped pajamas, which are rolled up above his ankles; he is barefoot. A silver whistle hangs from his belt, tied by a string. (He will be seen wearing this whistle in every scene.) Natural sounds such as the sea and wind (loud) and music (dissonant violin, etc.) throughout the shot.

Full shot, closer, of CARL. He is coming toward the camera. He picks up two identical shells, looks at them for a moment, then puts them in his left pocket. Continuing a few yards more along the water's edge, he spies something in a clump of grass to his right (screen left). He bends over and picks up two dolls roughly the same size. He examines them carefully—one in each hand—turning them over several times, looking from the face of one doll to the other. Then, with a violent gesture, he throws one doll back on the ground and puts the other one, head down, in his right pocket (the doll's legs stick up). Then he slowly brings his hands together in front of his chest, and smiles. The camera stays on him; he remains absolutely still.

Very long shot, from behind, of MARTIN and LENA. They are walking farther down the beach. (CARL has been following them.) MARTIN is nearer the water (screen left). LENA wears a black knit tank suit with a V-neck and is barefoot; MARTIN has on tan pants with the legs rolled up to the top of his calves, a white shirt with the sleeves rolled up above his elbows, and sandals; he is carrying a white sweater that belongs to LENA. The mood between them seems relaxed. Since they are much

66

too far away for us, realistically, to hear what they are saying, their lines in this shot, spoken in a low, intimate tone, amount to voice-over dialogue.

LENA

I don't believe in your holy fool.

MARTIN

Don't hate him.

LENA

I *don't* hate Carl. I never did.

MARTIN stops to remove his sandals, after which—turning—he looks back in CARL's direction (toward the camera). Seeing CARL standing still, he thrusts the sweater at LENA and retraces his steps rapidly. As he approaches CARL, the camera moves forward very slowly. LENA remains where she is, in the background of the shot. The sound of the sea comes up; the music stays at the same volume.

Reverse shot (frontal, from MARTIN's point of view) of CARL. He is immobile, a wide smile frozen on his face. MARTIN enters the shot, stands next to CARL (screen right).

MARTIN

Is something wrong? Do you want to go home?

CARL shakes his head emphatically, but doesn't change the smile.

MARTIN

Want to stay here?

CARL shakes his head again. MARTIN, perplexed, slowly circles (from screen right to screen left) around CARL's unmoving figure. He gestures with his right hand toward the water.

MARTIN

It's a beautiful day.

CARL, still with his painful smile-mask, doesn't move. MARTIN, coming around from behind him, now stands in profile on CARL's right (screen left).

MARTIN

People smile when they feel good . . . Maybe you feel good.

CARL shakes his head, still not modifying the smile.

Reverse angle (the camera is behind MARTIN and CARL): wide shot, with the two men in the foreground, MARTIN in profile

screen right and CARL (seen from behind) screen left. In the background of the shot, LENA is approaching slowly, obviously upset. MARTIN glances at LENA, who looks only at CARL. CARL behaves as if he doesn't see LENA. She reaches them, gazing all the while at CARL.

                              LENA
      (*Softly*) Make him stop!

MARTIN turns his head away. LENA doesn't take her eyes off CARL.

Reverse angle (LENA's point of view): close-up of CARL, still smiling. Hold for a few seconds.

The camera tracks back rapidly, until CARL becomes a small ▼ figure standing on the beach.

Wide shot, high angle, of KAREN sunbathing on a rock—she wears a dark bathing suit—with the sea in the background. She looks up (screen left) and shades her eyes. She is looking off-screen in the direction of MARTIN and LENA, who now enter the shot from the left, at the water's edge (toward the rear of the shot). KAREN stands up, and comes toward LENA and MARTIN. The camera follows.

                             KAREN
      Isn't it beautiful here?

                              LENA
      You'll catch cold.

LENA hands KAREN her white sweater. Mechanically KAREN starts to put it on, while speaking. The camera circles to KAREN's right; she is now in the foreground of the shot, with her back partly to the camera. MARTIN and LENA, facing each other (he screen left, she screen right) occupy the middle ground of the shot.

KAREN

What have you decided?

LENA

Let's stay another week.

KAREN looks quizzically at MARTIN. He turns toward her and smiles faintly.

MARTIN

Yes, stay.

KAREN looks at both for a moment.

KAREN

Where's Carl?

LENA points down the beach, in the direction from which they have come (CARL is not visible); her tone is sarcastic.

LENA

He's taken root in the sand. He's smiling.

MARTIN

(*Sharply*) Don't!

Very long shot of CARL on the beach (from the trio's point of view), still not moving—over which we hear LENA's voice, replying to MARTIN.

LENA'S VOICE

I know why you keep him with you. It's not to help Carl . . . It's cruel!

▲ Back to close-up of CARL, still frozen in the same smile.

Reverse angle: medium frontal shot of KAREN. (She and MARTIN have walked back to where CARL stands; LENA has remained where they were and is not visible again in this sequence.) KAREN is staring (at CARL) with fascination and alarm. Music up.

Wide shot. We see the living room of the Sandler apartment in Stockholm. ANNA, alone, wearing only her white underpants, walks across the room in the direction of the dining room; she is holding a tambourine to her right ear, shaking it in an irregular rhythm as she walks. Abruptly, she drops the tambourine and disappears around the corner—screen left—into the hallway leading to the front door. The image holds for several moments. Then the child reappears, awkwardly pulling a large black sweater over her head; it obviously belongs to an adult, and comes down to below her knees. After she has put it on, she places herself in a rigid position (in the left half of the shot)—her back against the wall, just this side of the entrance to the hallway. She stares in the direction of the camera, and doesn't move. Same music continues.

Back to previous medium frontal shot of KAREN. Without turning her head, she speaks to MARTIN (who is off-screen).

> KAREN
> Why does he smile?

Wide shot of all three. MARTIN glances at CARL, then turns to face KAREN; he is to her right, with his back to the water. She is staring at CARL.

> MARTIN
> Some feeling of pleasure sets it off, I suppose. But when that fades . . .

Talking, MARTIN does not see CARL come unfrozen. CARL slowly ambles off, out of the shot. KAREN turns in the direction that CARL has gone.

Very wide shot (from KAREN's point of view). CARL has entered the water and is wading out; the water (very shallow for several yards) is already above his knees.

MARTIN
(*Off*) . . . he sometimes gets stuck.

Back to KAREN and MARTIN, who turns and sees what is happening. MARTIN leaves KAREN (the camera pans to follow him) and runs into the water, moving diagonally from the right foreground of the image to the rear left. CARL, in the rear of the shot (and seen from the back), continues his determined march into the sea; the water is now up to his hips.

Reverse angle: medium shot of KAREN, watching. She seems cold and pulls the white sweater around her.

Very wide shot. MARTIN has reached CARL, both men are up to their waist in the water. MARTIN roughly grabs CARL, turns him around, and starts leading him out (toward the camera). CARL follows—awkwardly, docilely.

20. Woods. Two days later: early afternoon

Very wide shot. We are in a clearing in the woods, a natural enclosure bounded by a number of fallen or partially uprooted trees (the result of a storm), many with their huge complex roots exposed or even up-ended. In the rear of the shot, CARL is lying on his back, stretched out along the trunk of a large fallen tree—about five feet off the ground. He wears his striped pajamas. With his right hand he shades his eyes; in his left hand he holds an empty soft-drink bottle. The strong, cool-looking shadows in this scene contrast with the bright, shadowless, hot feeling of the preceding sequence. Natural sounds: birds, insects, etc. When after a few seconds we hear MARTIN's voice (speaking in a low tone, i.e., much closer to the camera than CARL is), CARL turns his head—as if he has heard, too.

MARTIN
(Off) You seem in a bad mood.

Wide shot. We see KAREN—it is to her that MARTIN's words are addressed—who wears a matching white knit pants and top, standing beside an upturned tree. With a stick she is scraping absentmindedly but sharply at the mud encrusted on the huge roots. She turns toward MARTIN (off-screen).

KAREN
Sorry. I usually am . . .
(Pause)
I hate my discontents.

73

She comes forward (toward the camera), drops to the ground on her knees, then sits on her heels Japanese-style. The camera moves back and we now see MARTIN too. (She is about five feet from MARTIN.) It's the end of a picnic. There is a white table-cloth on the ground, a wicker hamper, paper plates with remnants of food. MARTIN wears the same sweater as in sequences 8 and 9, light tan pants, and boots. He is lying on the ground, propped up on one elbow, next to the tablecloth; nearby is a small tree stump. He partly turns to look at KAREN; his manner, teasing yet casual, suggests for the first time some intimacy between them.

KAREN

I want to be good.

MARTIN

Why?

KAREN

I want to be what I admire.

MARTIN

Why not want to be what you are?

KAREN

It's hard to give up wanting to 'become' . . . *You* haven't done it.

MARTIN laughs softly.

MARTIN

No . . .

KAREN

What do *you* want to become? I'm sure it's not to be—good.

MARTIN shakes his head.

74

MARTIN

No, not that. Never that . . .

Back to CARL, a closer shot (but on same axis); he is still lying on top of the fallen tree trunk. He holds his hand in front of his face, and looks at it as infants do in their cribs.

MARTIN

(*Off*) When I was younger, I wanted to be . . . wonderful . . . amazing . . . magnificent . . . (*Laughs.*) I was.

Back to wide two-shot of KAREN and MARTIN. She has moved closer—still sitting on the ground—to where MARTIN is half reclining.

KAREN

And now?

MARTIN

I want to become someone who isn't wonderful.

After a pause, KAREN looks up in the direction of CARL (off-camera).

KAREN

Can he understand us?

Another shot of CARL. He is sitting up now, his legs hanging down, banging the empty bottle against the tree trunk.

MARTIN

(*Off*) Oh, Carl adores conversations like this! They're the only kind he really likes . . .

Back to medium shot of MARTIN and KAREN. KAREN is poised rather stiffly, MARTIN seems supremely relaxed. He smiles again.

MARTIN

You'll see what I mean if he starts talking. Carl also wants to be good.

KAREN

You're making fun of me.

MARTIN

(*Tenderly*) No.

KAREN looks at CARL (off-screen), then back at MARTIN.

KAREN

He can *really* follow what people say?

MARTIN

If he wants to . . .

Long shot of CARL from a different angle. He's now standing on the fallen tree trunk. He slowly makes his way down the trunk, coming closer to where MARTIN and KAREN are. (He is still about twenty-five feet from them, when he reaches the lower end of the trunk.) He turns and faces KAREN, half pointing at her.

Cut to shot of KAREN (in foreground) and MARTIN—from CARL's point of view. Not sure of what CARL means, KAREN points to herself.

Back to CARL. He reaches into the pocket of his pajamas and takes out a small black rock. Holding the rock, he almost smiles at KAREN; then he solemnly throws it in her direction.

Close shot of the rock landing in the grass near KAREN. Her hand comes into the shot and picks it up.

Wide two-shot, from CARL's point of view: KAREN (in foreground), still sitting on her heels, with MARTIN just behind her (and screen left). KAREN feels excited—flattered—by CARL's first signs of interest. She picks up the stone, looks at it, almost melodramatically presses it to her breast.

MARTIN

He likes you.

KAREN gazes at CARL, trying lamely and perhaps too directly to maintain the unexpected contact.

Full shot of CARL, from KAREN's point of view. He nods, and makes a small, ineffectual gesture with his hand (as if to stop KAREN's response), and turning slightly, moves into the shadowy branches of the tree trunk on which he is standing.

Very long shot of a slope at the far end of the clearing. LENA comes into view; she wears matching pants and a short-sleeve tunic of dark wool. She has been gathering flowers, and holds several bunches.

Back to the picnic site: MARTIN, nearer the camera, stretched out on the ground on his back, his head leaning against the small stump, and KAREN, behind him, sitting upright somewhat awkwardly. LENA enters the shot—from the left—and crouches down. Smiling, she gives one bunch of flowers to MARTIN, who receives them without any change of expression, then one to KAREN, whose tender smile is as eloquent as she can make it (she is aware of MARTIN's lack of response). LENA does not show any reaction either to MARTIN's lack of response or to KAREN's effusive pleasure. As soon as LENA has handed out the two bunches of flowers, she stands again. She turns and—with the camera tilting up (so KAREN and MARTIN are eliminated from the shot)—goes to the tree.

Medium shot of CARL, sitting on the lower end of the tree trunk, his legs dangling down a foot above the ground; he seems dejected. LENA enters the shot, hands CARL the last bunch of flowers, then quickly turns away (leaving the shot) as if she did not want to see his response. CARL holds the flowers for a moment, then opens his hand and lets them fall onto the ground.

Back to wide shot of the picnic site. MARTIN and KAREN are still there; LENA rejoins them (coming into the shot on the left) and sinks down next to MARTIN. LENA, sighing with pleasure, puts her arms around MARTIN, hugs him, buries her face on his chest, strokes his hair; they are in the foreground. Mid-ground in the shot, KAREN sits, looking down on them benevolently, though she also feels awkward. LENA's face is radiant. She reaches out to touch KAREN, to include her.

>   LENA
> How good we are together. I love you both so much.

KAREN, who has been sitting tensely on her heels, relaxes and puts her legs in a more comfortable position. LENA turns on her back, putting her head on MARTIN's chest. She takes KAREN's and MARTIN's hand.

>   LENA
> Sometimes I feel so full of love . . . Standing in a crowded bus, with a stranger's hand above mine clutching the same pole, I've felt a sudden desire to kiss that hand.

Medium long shot of CARL, climbing down from the tree.

>   LENA
> (Off) I know I'd horrify everyone on the bus if I did it. It would be much more shocking than if I suddenly *bit* someone's hand.

Medium shot of MARTIN and LENA.

LENA

It's as if we're all under some terrible sentence. Not allowed to show our love for each other.

MARTIN's eyes remain closed when he speaks.

MARTIN

If you're asking whether I love you—you know that I do.

LENA lets go of MARTIN's hand. He lifts his head, but still doesn't open his eyes.

MARTIN

Why did you do that?

LENA

It frightens me when *you* talk about love.

Wide shot of all three. KAREN gazes at MARTIN and LENA with a pained expression. Then, on impulse, she bends over and kisses LENA's hand. LENA smiles.

LENA

I'm not a stranger.

KAREN

No, not you. I am. You make me feel ashamed of myself. I'm so stingy with my feelings.

During KAREN's last words, the camera moves, so that MARTIN is now in the center of the shot. He opens his eyes, looking first at LENA and then at KAREN.

MARTIN

Watch out. You want everything to be simpler than it is.

KAREN

I've already warned Lena against you. Are you warning me against her?

MARTIN

We should all be warned against each other. ▲

Wide shot: CARL, having left his tree, slowly walks to the center of the clearing. Even more slowly, he lowers himself into a squatting position some distance away from MARTIN, KAREN, and LENA—watching them sadly, meditatively—the very image of the person who is excluded.

LENA

(*Off*) Including him? ▼

MARTIN

(*Off*) No, not Carl . . . Why don't you try giving *him* some of your inexhaustible supply of love?

Back to wide shot of all three. LENA sits up with a violent movement.

LENA

You're hateful!

KAREN looks from one to the other.

KAREN

Please—both of you! We were so peaceful before.

Very long shot of MARTIN, KAREN, and LENA in the background, and CARL (from the back) squatting mid-ground—taken from the top of the hillock. Fade. Several seconds of blackness. ▲

21. *Veranda of Martin's cottage. Next day: afternoon*

Medium shot of CARL's hands, grasping two metal ring grips that hang on ropes from the veranda ceiling. Slowly his head comes into view, from the bottom of the frame. He is chinning himself—laboriously.

Full shot. CARL—wearing his striped pajamas, barefoot—lets go of the ring he holds with his right hand and hangs loose with his left arm, dangling limply for a moment, then letting go and dropping to the thin mat on the floor of the veranda. CARL picks up the light metal bar lying on the wood floor beside the mat, and begins to exercise. It is an extremely simple exercise, which he does mechanically and with excessive effort. It consists of moving from a lying to a sitting position with his arms extended, holding the bar; then, after a pause, stretching forward to press the bar against the soles of his feet—and back again . . . . Just behind CARL, also facing the camera, is MARTIN, who wears pants, a white T-shirt, and sneakers. He is sitting on his heels.

Medium shot: CARL doing the exercise, MARTIN behind him. Each time CARL sits up and pauses, he blocks MARTIN. It is at this moment, the third time CARL goes through the exercise, that MARTIN says his line.

                    MARTIN
          Tell me when you're tired.

CARL does the exercise once more, then gets up and moves to the veranda railing. He shakes out his hands once or twice (as dancers do). MARTIN stands too and moves behind him; he watches CARL intently, except for one moment, when his attention seems to wander and he looks out toward the woods. CARL begins, very slowly, what resembles an exercise at the practice bar. But he has hardly gotten into it when MARTIN, behind him, catches his ankle—as if to help him extend his leg. CARL pulls away and turns his head violently toward MARTIN.

Cut to closer shot (on the movement of CARL's head); CARL looks at MARTIN.

> CARL
> I never wanted to dance.

Medium shot of the two.

> MARTIN
> (*Gently*) I know.

CARL continues looking dumbly at MARTIN. Trying to change the mood, MARTIN leaves the railing and returns to the exercise mat (going out of the shot). CARL doesn't move, but cocks his head like a puppy to follow MARTIN's movements (off-screen).

Wide shot. We see MARTIN doing deep knee bends. He looks over at CARL.

> MARTIN
> Try it with me.

He extends his arm and steers CARL back into his position, in front of him on the mat. Somnambulistically, CARL starts doing the deep knee bends with MARTIN.

> MARTIN
> Exercise is good . . . You don't have to think about it.

After doing it a third or fourth time, CARL suddenly stops the exercise while in squatting position; he has gone blank, immobile again. MARTIN, behind him, goes on a moment longer.

Music throughout sequence.

22. Outside Martin's cottage. Later that afternoon

Close medium shot (frontal—similar to last shot of previous sequence) of CARL's head and now naked upper torso. He looks vacant, disoriented. Different music from previous scene: abrasive 'mad theme.' At one moment CARL looks up, as if he heard something in a tree.

Very wide shot, which shows what's happening. At the top of a slope, MARTIN—dressed as in the previous sequence, except that he has put on a checked shirt over his T-shirt (the sleeves are rolled up above the elbows)—is bathing CARL in an ordinary-size metal bathtub. MARTIN's movements are gentle, without being sensual. He soaps CARL's back and neck. CARL, completely passive, seems very tense: his back and neck are particularly rigid. In this shot, CARL and MARTIN are mid-ground, with CARL nearer the camera and in profile; CARL is facing toward the left side of the frame. We see the veranda and part of the cottage in the rear of the image (about thirty feet behind them).

Change of shot. Full frontal view of CARL, with MARTIN behind him, still washing his back. At the bottom of the frame, we see CARL's naked toes sticking up out of the bathtub. Suddenly CARL twists himself, doubles up, and plunges his head and most of his body under water. A mock drowning or a real one?

MARTIN rests one hand on the rim of the tub, pushes back a strand of hair with the other. He is waiting for CARL to surface. Thirty, forty seconds go by; it should, and will, seem long. Under water, CARL (all we see is a portion of his bony back) doesn't move. MARTIN starts to get worried. He reaches out his hand to touch CARL's back, then pulls it away; he doesn't dare interfere. He waits, sitting on his heels. The music stops. At least another forty seconds pass. Then, like a monster rising from the sea, CARL unfolds himself and lifts his head and upper torso out of the water; his wet hair covers his eyes. (Note: the whole action takes place within one shot, and the audience

must feel that there is no trickery, that the actor who plays
CARL really is staying under water for an extraordinarily long
time, which will be true.)

Cut to a medium shot (still frontal) of CARL's face and upper
torso. He pushes his hair away from his eyes. It is as if he has
been reborn. He looks peaceful now; he looks up shyly, almost
smiling at MARTIN.

Wide shot (still frontal). MARTIN looks at CARL as if he wants
to say something, but can't. MARTIN prefers to continue the
bath. He reaches into the water, searching for the bar of soap
he had dropped when CARL went under. He can't find it. After

a few moments, he gives up and resumes scrubbing CARL's back —without the soap. CARL's body is relaxed now. CARL reaches his hand into the water, easily retrieves the soap from between his legs, and hands it to MARTIN, smiling fondly at him. CARL seems released; on his face is a beatific expression we have never seen before. He nods several times to himself. Music.

Very long shot: reverse angle of second shot in this sequence. The camera is in front of the cottage. In the background of the shot we see MARTIN (his back to the camera) on his knees finishing washing CARL. Then he stands up and helps CARL rise in the bathtub, puts a bathrobe on him, and then helps him step out of the tub onto the ground. (CARL is never seen entirely naked. He has been wearing black wool bikini briefs in the tub, which we see when he stands. Although the bathrobe he now wears hangs open, from the angle at which the two figures are seen, CARL's body is mostly covered.)

Now MARTIN stands before CARL—screen right—and dries his chest with a large towel. (Both bathrobe and towel were on the ground beside the tub.) CARL lets himself be attended to, without moving. Next, MARTIN slips CARL's briefs down to his ankles; CARL lifts one foot, then the other; MARTIN tosses the briefs aside. Stooping, he quickly dries CARL's hips and legs, then helps him into the bottoms of his striped pajamas. The two figures, fairly far away, are seen mostly in profile—fac-

ing each other. About halfway through the shot, the fairly neutral sound atmosphere of this sequence—birds, low wind, etc.—slowly fades. Over the action of drying CARL and putting his pajama bottoms on him, we now hear the sound (up) of a fire crackling and voices 'over.' It is the beginning of the next sequence.

> KAREN'S VOICE
> Carl only started to dance after he met you, didn't he?

> MARTIN'S VOICE
> No . . . When I discovered him, he was already a student at the school. He still wasn't sure about dancing—but he'd wanted to go abroad—and when he got a scholarship here his parents made him accept it.

Cut to the next sequence just as MARTIN pulls the bathrobe off the motionless CARL (to finish dressing him).

23. *A clearing in the woods. A little later*
    (early evening)

Medium shot of MARTIN, in the same clothes as in the preceding sequence. Sound of crackling fire is louder; it continues throughout the sequence.

MARTIN

MARTIN

I took Carl to see them last October. They don't know he hasn't danced for thirteen years. They don't even see what's happened to him.

Very wide shot. It is dark. Mid-ground in the shot is a bonfire. On the far side of the bonfire are MARTIN, KAREN, and LENA. MARTIN is between the two women; he sits on a log. KAREN— wearing dark pants, a heavy white turtleneck sweater, and a denim jacket—sits on the ground just to his left (screen right). LENA, wearing a beige jacket and pants, sits on another log, to the right of MARTIN and KAREN; she gives the impression of being somewhat separated from them. (It is as if MARTIN and KAREN are the couple in this scene, and LENA is the outsider.)

KAREN

Why?

Cut to reverse angle shot: to show CARL, who is on the other side of the fire, his face partly obscured by the flames. He is lying on his back, on a dark blanket, at the foot of a tree; he wears his khaki jacket and striped pajama bottoms. CARL has his eyes closed; he opens them and turns his head toward the three (i.e., toward the camera).

CARL

They're too old.

(*Pause*)

I love them.

Back to medium shot (from CARL's point of view) of MARTIN and KAREN.

MARTIN

Go on, Carl.

Back to medium shot of CARL. He sits up. His face is animated; he is looking at MARTIN (off-camera).

CARL

You tell. I like to hear. Tell the story. How we went there.

CARL busies himself with pulling the blanket out from underneath him.

Medium shot of MARTIN. He seems to be hesitating; he gives CARL (off-screen) an odd look. Then he starts the story. Arhythmic music begins here: MARTIN's accompaniment.

> MARTIN
> They're monstrous. But at least once a year Carl insists on visiting them. He wants to love them and kill the monster in himself.

Back to medium shot of CARL. As he speaks, he pulls the blanket up around his waist.

> CARL
> I don't want to kill any monsters. (*Glances at* MARTIN.) Not even you.

Very wide shot of all four, with CARL—his back to the camera —in the foreground. Mid-ground is the fire, on the far side of which are the others. LENA pokes at the fire with a branch to help it burn better; KAREN's attention is divided between MARTIN and CARL. MARTIN continues in a slightly singsong voice.

> MARTIN
> They live together in the forest like two old witches. You know how married couples often come to resemble each other eventually? Already, years ago, they looked like brother and sister.

Medium long shot of MARTIN and KAREN, with the fire in front of them—favoring MARTIN. There is something malevolent in his expression.

> MARTIN
> It's gone much further now. Each year it becomes harder to tell which is which. Identical, high, quavering voices

come out of their toothless mouths. The same length of thin silver hair covers the patches of bald scalp on both heads.

Cut to same medium shot of CARL, pulling more of the blanket around him.

MARTIN
(*Off*) The same shapeless torsos . . .

CARL looks up (off-screen), as he finishes bringing the blanket up over his back onto his shoulders, at MARTIN.

CARL
Don't stop.

Back to MARTIN in medium shot: he glances oddly in CARL's direction (as if CARL is behaving in an unexpected way), then continues. He speaks faster now, as if he is eager to get through the story; his tone is theatrical.

MARTIN
Even Carl can scarcely tell them apart now. If he approaches the bent figure sitting by the fireplace munching on a piece of dried herring and says "Mother," it may reply irritably, "I am your father." If he turns to the figure wearing a shabby smock, puffing on a pipe, and starts off, "Father?", it's likely to scream, "I'm your mother!"

24. Hotel room. Same time

Sequence shot: a wide shot of LENA and KAREN. They are sitting on their beds, facing each other: KAREN, cross-legged, on the left side of the shot, LENA on the right. Their clothes are those of

the previous sequence. LENA, gazing at KAREN, starts talking the moment the sequence starts—picking up where MARTIN left off. Her tone, as she tells the story, is quite different from his. She is unconvincingly animated.

LENA

When Martin arrives with Carl, the first thing they ask is whether either has brought them any candy. Then they reproach Carl for not sending them any money. They accuse Martin of having kidnapped their son and pocketed all his earnings. They complain that Martin and Carl have brought dirt into the house on their shoes —snapping more viciously at Carl, because they're still afraid of Martin. They remember that, for years, when Carl was dancing, Martin wouldn't ever let him visit them.

KAREN

(*Imploringly*) Don't tell me any more.

LENA's tone becomes even more lighthearted.

LENA

No, listen, it's funny. I mean, they would be comic if they weren't so horrible.

KAREN lowers her head in anguish.

25. Clearing. Immediately after

Medium shot of KAREN, raising her head (from the position it was in at the end of the previous sequence). She looks (off-screen) at MARTIN.

KAREN

(*Gravely*) Go on.

Medium shot of CARL.

MARTIN

(*Off*) This last time we went, I lost my temper and denounced them.

Back to same medium shot of MARTIN and the fire as in sequence 23.

MARTIN

"Look at your son!" I shouted. "Don't you see he's ill? How can you be so selfish?" . . . Then one of them, his mother, I think—but maybe it was his father—started whimpering. And the other one sprang to his spouse's defense, screaming, "*You* look!"

Wide shot of all four, with the camera behind CARL. Sitting up,

93

he pulls the blanket over his head. MARTIN's recitative continues without pause.

> MARTIN
> "Look what you're doing! How dare you upset us! How dare you make us worry!"

> CARL
> They were right. You shouldn't worry them.

CARL's voice is muffled and slow. KAREN looks at CARL.

> KAREN
> I hate them for not loving Carl.

LENA, who has not been participating, looks up and speaks sharply—partly to the others, partly to herself.

> LENA
> It's obscene to live so long!

Full shot of CARL (from the point of view of MARTIN and KAREN). We see that he is entirely covered by the blanket—as if he were inside a tent.

> CARL
> Some people can't die.

Back to wide shot of the four, with CARL (his back to the camera) in the foreground, the bonfire mid-ground, and the three others gazing at CARL.

26. Hotel room. Next day

▼

Long shot—the camera is inside the room—of LENA and KAREN. LENA is sitting up on her bed, in the rear of the shot, reading and taking notes. She is wearing a light cotton shirt and shorts. There is a glass of water and a bottle of pills on the night table. In the foreground, KAREN, sitting in an easy chair, is manicuring her nails. She wears beige pants and a long-sleeve, light cotton blouse of Indian cut. LENA stops, takes off her glasses.

This stupid headache of mine. I'm getting up—

She puts her legs over the edge of the bed. KAREN looks up.

Why? You shouldn't work now. Sleep a little.

LENA puts her legs up on the bed and lies back. KAREN, surprised that LENA has done what she has suggested, is concerned. She gets up, goes over to LENA, and removes the book, papers, and clipboard from the bed. LENA has her eyes shut.

Camera pans with KAREN as she goes to the window and closes the curtains. We hear the telephone ringing. She turns—the camera follows—and rushes for the phone. (It is on the desk, near the French doors.) KAREN picks up the phone, listens for a moment, then replies—softly but urgently, cupping the receiver and her mouth with her hand so as not to disturb LENA (who is not in the shot).

Yes . . . Yes, I know who it is . . . Yes . . . I'll be right down.

▲ She replaces the phone on the hook.

27. Grounds of hotel. Minutes later

Very long shot of KAREN, just outside the main rear doors of the hotel. With her is a man—probably the desk clerk who phoned her—pointing. He goes back inside the hotel and she hurries down two steps and along the path (in the direction of the camera). It is a bright day, sharpening the contrast between the darkened room of the last shot and the light and sense of space in this shot. Natural sounds throughout.

Long shot, reverse angle: CARL, partly turned away, standing at the top of a flight of stone steps. (The steps are behind him in the shot; in the rear of the image is the sea, small boats, etc.) CARL wears a black overcoat, almost ankle length, and heavy shoes (no socks); his tan pants and light-colored shirt unbuttoned at the wrists are scarcely visible. He looks lost—and as if he can't decide whether to bolt or wait. After a few seconds, KAREN, out of breath, enters the shot.

KAREN

Carl!

She stops. CARL looks at her apprehensively. He keeps his hands in his pockets.

KAREN

Did you come to see me? I'm glad . . .

CARL looks at her, unsure. Then he looks away. KAREN is unclear about how to approach him. She takes two steps backward, not wishing to overwhelm him—and awkwardly extends her hand.

KAREN

We can go for a walk.

CARL doesn't move. KAREN takes another step backward, waits for him, then takes a step toward him. She doesn't know what to do.

KAREN

Is Martin here?

CARL suddenly looks very angry (this was just what she shouldn't have said), turns away violently, and, throwing her one fierce look over his right shoulder, hurries down the stone stairs (and out of the shot).

Carl!

She runs after him.

28. Bathhouse near hotel. Minutes later

Very long shot of the changing-room area. CARL, having escaped from KAREN, is standing indecisively on a large wood platform for sunbathers a foot below a ⊏-shaped row of changing rooms—looking about, barely managing to master his panic. (No one except CARL is in the shot, and the doors of all the cabins in the shot are closed.) In his long black overcoat, CARL looks the cliché image of a sex maniac on the prowl. Then a heavily built young blond woman in a bathing suit comes out of one of the cabins. To leave the area, she has to walk fairly near where CARL is standing; she seems frightened by him. CARL stares after her with curiosity.

Long shot of KAREN (from CARL's point of view), as she arrives at the entrance at a run, out of breath. She stops on the threshold.

KAREN

Carl!

Full shot of CARL (from KAREN's point of view). He jumps up onto the walk that skirts the row of cabins—and clumsily runs along it; once at the far end, he bangs on several cabin doors to try to get inside and hide.

Closer shot of CARL banging desperately on one door after another, fearfully looking over his shoulder in KAREN's direction (toward the camera). When the sixth or seventh door does yield to his banging—unlike all the others, it is open—he has moved past it before he realizes the difference.

Back to the previous full shot (now a very long one). CARL darts into the cabin and slams the door behind him.

Natural sounds throughout this sequence.

29. *Changing room. A moment later*

Medium high-angle shot of the dark interior of the cabin, with soft-edged stripes of light on the floor. On the right side of the shot, CARL is crouching in a corner with his head in his arms. We hear the sound of the door opening. CARL is caught in a flood of light. He sits up, and throws his hands before his face to shield his eyes. He looks terrified.

Medium shot of KAREN in the doorway. (Camera is inside the cabin. Not a low-angle shot.)

KAREN

Please get up.

There is no answer from CARL.

KAREN

Is it the light?

Still no answer.

KAREN

We *can't* stay here.

Back to CARL. He turns his head away, still keeping his face covered. A shadow slowly covers half his body. (KAREN has entered and shut the door halfway.) He turns back and looks furtively, less frightened now, at KAREN.

Shot of KAREN (from CARL's point of view) kneeling down in front of him. She looks very troubled.

KAREN

I wish I could *talk* to you.

There is no response from CARL.

▼ Medium close-up of CARL. He opens his mouth, wets his lips, then speaks—fairly distinctly.

CARL

Do you think there's more good than bad?

Medium shot of KAREN and CARL. KAREN is astonished.

KAREN

I don't know . . .

CARL pauses, then speaks again, with animation.

CARL

But say.

KAREN

There's more good.

CARL

That's what I believe, too.
(*Pause*)
I don't *really* believe it. I think there's more bad.
(*Pause*)
But I like to hear a different opinion.

KAREN

Maybe you'll change your mind.

CARL shakes his head.

CARL

No! I can't! I can't think. That's my problem.

KAREN

Look, you're thinking now.

CARL shakes his head again. KAREN is silent, not knowing what
to reply.   ▲

Suddenly CARL's face is flooded with light; someone has opened
the door. He groans with terror.

CARL

Oh, no!

KAREN hurls herself against him, to shield him from the in-
truder.

Full shot of the doorway. The blond woman is peering in. She
closes the door.

Back to CARL (from KAREN's point of view): a closer medium shot. CARL recovers his composure, such as it is.

> KAREN
> (*Off*) Don't be afraid.

CARL smiles wistfully.

> CARL
> It's all right. People who are afraid are usually good people.

He lowers his voice.

> CARL
> I'm afraid of being bad.

Reverse angle, close medium shot of KAREN (from CARL's point of view). KAREN has her head down and looks as if she's about to cry.

> CARL
> (*Off*) Don't cry.

KAREN looks up.

Back to close medium shot of CARL.

> CARL
> I'm always crying.
> (*Pause*)
> Try to understand. It makes me tremble when people don't understand me.

> KAREN
> (*Off*) Doesn't Martin understand you?

> CARL
> Yes. But Martin is my enemy.

Cut. Several seconds of blackness, over which we hear KAREN speaking.

KAREN

(*Off*) Come. I'll walk you . . . home.

30. *Living room of Sandler apartment. No particular time*

Full shot of ANNA, dressed in her white underpants, standing in the middle of the living room. She holds a small, old-fashioned coffee mill to her ear; she slowly turns the handle, wholly absorbed by the sound. Over this image we hear the voices (off) of KAREN and MARTIN. (It is the dialogue of the first part of the scene that we see continuing in sequence 31.)

KAREN'S VOICE

Carl finally talked to me.

MARTIN'S VOICE

Something very abstract, I suppose.

KAREN'S VOICE

(*Hesitantly*) Yes . . .

MARTIN'S VOICE

It usually is.

31. *Veranda of Martin's cottage. Later the same afternoon as sequence 29*

Sequence shot. Starts with medium long shot: KAREN is in the foreground. She is standing just behind a large wicker chair in which MARTIN is seated; we see only the top of the chair, not

103

MARTIN, at the beginning of the shot. CARL enters the shot; he is wearing the long black coat and heavy shoes of sequences 27–29: KAREN, too, wears the same clothes. CARL pauses before KAREN, then reaches out and awkwardly strokes her face.

> CARL
>
> (*Slowly*) I've never had a woman. Never.

KAREN is not at all afraid of CARL now, and does not even glance down at MARTIN (on her left). CARL abruptly leaves KAREN and lurches toward the camera.

The camera moves back, to make a wider shot; we see the three of them clearly. CARL stops a few feet in front of MARTIN. Now in the foreground of the shot, right side of the frame, CARL hunches against the outside wall of the house, and starts rhythmically kicking the base of the wall. (A reminder of ANNA's pounding on the windowpanes in sequence 6.) MARTIN appears not to be paying attention to what is happening (though that certainly can't be so).

KAREN comes from behind MARTIN's chair, goes toward CARL (i.e., toward the camera), and stands before him. He is still leaning against the wall, his right side to KAREN; he doesn't look at her. Perhaps there are tears in his eyes.

> KAREN
>
> (*Gently*) Carl?

When CARL doesn't answer, she turns to MARTIN (away from the camera), who is now watching.

> MARTIN
>
> What's the matter, Carl?

> CARL
>
> It's not perfect.

CARL continues kicking the wall with his foot (off-screen).

KAREN
(Bitterly) What does he mean, it's not perfect?

MARTIN
It's something he says often.

Hold on image a few seconds.

32. Outside an abandoned factory. Next day

Medium close-up of a car door being slammed shut; and
KAREN's hand.

Very long shot of MARTIN, KAREN, and LENA. They are already
out of the car, which is parked right next to the old factory
building. The camera tracks parallel to them—from right to
left—as they walk alongside the long wall of the factory, with
MARTIN in the lead. LENA wears a black wool turtleneck sweater
and black pants. KAREN wears leather pants and vest with a
long-sleeve white blouse and foulard. MARTIN wears tan corduroy pants, a grey sweater (the collar of his white shirt is showing), and hiking boots.

MARTIN
It's one of Carl's favorite places around here. He likes
buildings that have been abandoned.

LENA
(Coldly) Is that why we drove over here?

MARTIN ignores LENA's tone.

No. I like it too.

LENA is in a bad mood and is letting herself fall behind. KAREN keeps up with MARTIN. He reaches the door of the factory, opens it, and enters. KAREN has her back to LENA, who continues walking. She leaves the shot when she turns the corner of the factory building (left side of the shot), and we see her shadow move along the wall for a moment after that. MARTIN has already entered the factory; KAREN—about to follow him—looks behind her.

KAREN
Lena?

There is no answer. KAREN continues into the factory.

The natural sounds throughout this sequence and the next are somewhat exaggerated or distorted: the slamming of the car door, steps on gravel and/or broken glass, etc.

33. Inside the factory. Minutes later

Very long shot of MARTIN and KAREN. They are in the rear of the image, walking silently through the ground floor of the factory. They cross diagonally—from screen left to screen right—through the factory's mysterious, open space.

A full shot of MARTIN and KAREN. They have come down a long passageway, which brings them to a crude set of wooden stairs littered with broken glass.

They stop. KAREN looks at MARTIN, who appears lost in thought.

KAREN
Martin?

He looks at her.

KAREN

Are you thinking about Carl?

MARTIN

Some of the time I try *not* to think about Carl . . .

The camera pans to show MARTIN starting up the steps; KAREN follows him. (Now their backs are to the camera.)

MARTIN

I was thinking about—

Since the camera, which is near the bottom of the stairs, stays level, they quickly go out of sight (and earshot). We hear the sound of footsteps on broken glass. The camera shows the empty staircase for another moment.

Wide shot of a portion of the bleak, scarred interior wall of the factory's ground floor. LENA comes from around a corner, walking slowly. She seems lost. She sees the stairs that MARTIN and KAREN climbed in the previous shot. As she puts her foot on the first step, she looks up to the top of the stairs (off-screen) and calls out softly.

LENA

Karen?

Wide shot. We are on the second floor of the factory. In the background is a narrow doorway (no door) in which after a moment, LENA appears. She pauses on the threshold, looking in hesitantly, then sees KAREN and MARTIN (off-screen).

LENA

(*Sarcastically*) Tell me if I'm intruding!

Wide shot of KAREN and MARTIN. They are leaning on their elbows on two sides of some kind of low, square scaffolding. They seem to have been talking with intensity. KAREN, whose back is to a window, looks up—in LENA's direction—with embarrassment.

LENA enters the shot. But before she can speak, everyone is startled by the sound of some gravel thrown hard—from outside—against the window behind KAREN. KAREN turns to look; so does MARTIN.

Very high-angle long shot, through the window, of CARL standing below. He is gesturing agitatedly. He has on baggy tan pants and a heavy loose sweater; the bottoms of his trousers are rolled up above the ankles and he wears shoes but, as usual, no socks. . . . He stoops to pick up another handful of gravel.

Medium long shot of MARTIN and LENA. Turning back from the window, MARTIN seems concerned.

MARTIN

Let's go down.

LENA

He's all right. He won't go away.

MARTIN

He's upset.

MARTIN leaves the shot (walking toward the camera). LENA, who remains by the window, calls after him.

LENA

(*Furious*) Must he follow us everywhere?

The image holds for a moment—on LENA, immobilized with rage.

Natural sounds throughout this sequence, but distorted or exaggerated. The sound of the gravel hitting the window should be very sharp; the voices have a hollow sound or an echo, etc.

34. *Outside the factory. Minutes later*

Medium shot of CARL, in the near foreground: he is waiting outside. He is fiddling impatiently with the whistle he always carries. (It dangles on a string attached to his belt.) He is in profile, facing screen left. Visible behind him, in the background, is most of the length of the factory building. (This is not the same side by which MARTIN, KAREN, and LENA entered in sequence 32.) Then we see MARTIN come out through a small door; he hurries toward CARL—that is, toward the camera. When he reaches CARL, he is screen left. The two men face each other. CARL pulls on MARTIN's sleeve.

Women are wonderful. They're perfect. I wouldn't *want* to touch them—

In the background of the shot, we see LENA and KAREN emerging from the factory by the same door that MARTIN used. LENA walks slowly; KAREN stays a few steps behind her. MARTIN is aware that the two women are coming. CARL is desperate to keep MARTIN's attention a moment longer.

CARL
I might hurt them or make them sad.

LENA has arrived to within thirty feet of CARL and stops. KAREN has dropped farther behind, and stops too. CARL senses the menace and looks at LENA, then back to MARTIN—as if he expected MARTIN to explain or to intervene.

LENA
(*Shouting*) Go away!

CARL looks alarmed but he doesn't back off. LENA stoops, picks up a handful of gravel, and hurls it at him. CARL's face registers physical pain and bewilderment.

Change of shot, but same angle: LENA stands in the foreground; KAREN is still some distance behind her. (Neither MARTIN nor CARL are in the beginning of this shot.) The camera pans as LENA turns and walks screen right. MARTIN enters the shot and confronts her.

MARTIN

You shouldn't have done that.

LENA folds her arms defiantly and doesn't reply. MARTIN walks on past her (into the background of the shot): he is going to the car. LENA remains where and as she is. Then KAREN enters the shot—also from screen left—and walks behind LENA to stand just to her left (i.e., screen right); she is in profile. She stands very close to LENA, silent at first; she holds LENA lightly, leaning against her for a moment. LENA does not look at KAREN.

KAREN

(*Soothingly*) Let's go to the car.

LENA seems unreachable; she has become a statue.

LENA

I'll walk!

KAREN gives up and turns to follow MARTIN—who is still visible, in the rear of the shot, walking away from the camera. LENA stands, unmoving, for another moment. The figure of KAREN retreats into the background. Then, abruptly, as if she has now reached a decision, LENA strides off in the other direction—diagonally, toward the lower right of the frame. The camera pans to the right to keep up with her (losing KAREN and MARTIN). As she continues, we pick up CARL again. The camera stops panning when CARL (who is in mid-ground) is in the center of the image: LENA, closer to the camera than CARL is (i.e., she is in the foreground), walks in front of an astonished CARL. Passing fairly close to him, she behaves as if no one is there—and continues out of the image on the right. CARL, almost in full shot, remains alone in the frame. He looks to his right (screen left), the direction that MARTIN and KAREN have taken, then to his left (screen right), the direction in which LENA has just gone—considering whom to follow. Then he ambles off screen right.

35. Road. Fifteen minutes later

Very long shot of a car speeding down a country road. Natural sounds (slightly exaggerated) throughout the sequence.

Medium shot of KAREN and MARTIN in the car. The camera is inside, behind them. KAREN, her body held stiffly, is at the wheel; MARTIN is beside her. She is weaving about on the road and taking curves much too fast.

MARTIN

You drive badly.

KAREN

I can't help it.

KAREN turns her head for a moment to look at MARTIN.

112

KAREN

No . . . I suppose I want to.

Another wide shot of the speeding car. Sound of brakes, etc.

36. Exterior of the hotel, Some minutes later

Full shot of the car turning into the hotel driveway—it goes from right to left in the image—and coming to a sharp stop. We hear the squeaking of tires, the sound of brakes. Cut motor. In the background: the rear façade of the hotel.

Frontal two-shot of MARTIN and KAREN, through the windshield; the camera is on the hood. KAREN stretches, her hands pushing against the steering wheel (as if she had a backache), then leans against the seat loosely and throws her head back. MARTIN has turned to watch her. They haven't exchanged a word. Then we see him lean toward her, first putting his left arm over her shoulder; he is about to kiss her. KAREN pulls away. He sits back.

MARTIN'S VOICE

You're more like me than you admit. You don't want anything from anybody.

KAREN'S VOICE

No, I'm not like you . . . I still want something from myself.

(We don't see their lips moving. The tone of the voice-over lines is low, intimate.)

37. *Path in the woods (somewhere between Carl's cabin and the factory). A half hour later*

Long shot of LENA, walking slowly along a path. As she passes a tree, CARL jumps out heavily from behind it. She is less startled than one would have expected. CARL approaches her timidly. Natural sounds—especially wind, rustling leaves—throughout the sequence.

Medium shot of the two, facing each other—LENA screen left and CARL screen right. (She is on slightly higher ground than he.) He reaches into his pocket and gives her a letter. She examines the envelope, then looks at CARL.

LENA

From you?

CARL nods. She turns the letter over once, then hands it back to CARL.

LENA
(*Harshly*) Give it to Martin yourself.

Two-shot, favoring CARL. The camera is behind, and slightly above LENA; we see CARL frontally. Dismay and confusion show on his face. Then he thrusts the letter back into her hands, and runs away into the woods. The camera pans with him, then loses him.

Medium shot of LENA opening the envelope, taking out the letter, reading it. A look of sharp distress comes over her face. She reads it once more. Then she starts walking again.

Full shot of LENA from another angle. As she walks (slowly), she tears up the letter into small pieces, which she scatters on the path.

38. Near Carl's cabin. Late afternoon

Very long shot of CARL, with his cabin in the background of the shot. CARL, dressed as in sequences 3 and 11, is digging a large hole. The image is held for about ten seconds, during which time we hear KAREN's voice. Natural sounds.

> KAREN'S VOICE
> But it's not true you don't want anything from anybody.
> You want something from Carl.

39. Exterior of the hotel. Same as sequence 36

A shot of KAREN and MARTIN taken from outside the car (on KAREN's side), putting KAREN in the foreground and MARTIN behind her. KAREN looks straight ahead, not at MARTIN.

> KAREN
> What did you do to Carl?

> MARTIN
> I'm responsible for his being like this.

KAREN
I don't believe you.

40. *Near Carl's cabin. Sunset*

Medium long shot, a closer version of sequence 38, of CARL
digging the hole, then pausing—he leans against the shovel.
Natural sounds throughout the shot—the shovel in the earth,
CARL panting from exertion, etc.—over which we hear:

MARTIN'S VOICE
Don't you?

KAREN'S VOICE
Yes. I do . . . But I don't want to hate you.

Part of KAREN's line is obscured by the bang of CARL's shovel
hitting rock.

MARTIN'S VOICE
Now you sound like Carl.

41. Exterior of the hotel. Same as sequences 36 and 39

Two-shot of MARTIN and KAREN, still sitting in the car—favoring MARTIN.

> MARTIN
> I want to cure Carl.

42. Inside Carl's cabin. After sunset

Low-angle medium shot of CARL's bed, heaped with blankets, extremely messy. Music starts: flute solo.

> KAREN'S VOICE
> You want him to forgive you.

> MARTIN'S VOICE
> Oh, he's forgiven me many times—too many—and then he forgets.

CARL's left arm emerges from the blankets (now we see that he was there, lying in a semi-fetal position) and throws them off his head. He opens his eyes and raises his head, as if he had heard something.

> MARTIN'S VOICE
> That's part of his condition . . . No, I want to cure him. But I can't.

CARL lies there on his right side with his eyes open, vacant. Sound of a door opening: creaking. CARL looks up sharply.

Reverse angle: full shot, from CARL's viewpoint, of LENA ducking her head slightly to stand in the cabin doorway. The crude door behind her, made of boards nailed together, is half open. She is wearing the black sweater and pants of sequences 32, 33, 34, and 37. She hesitates a long moment, then she closes the door and takes a step inside.

LENA

(*Gently*) You think I don't like you. That's not true.

Full shot, from LENA's point of view. Now we see the interior of CARL's cabin. It is actually a former earth cellar—rectangular in shape and, as a place to live, tiny, cave-like, filthy and cluttered. There is a heavy fur rug on the floor; the only furniture is CARL's narrow bed (a worn, striped mattress on a plank mounted on bricks; no sheets; many blankets) and a small table beside the foot of the bed with a kerosene lamp, a cup of nuts, and an empty glass. The lamp is lit and casts strong shadows. Patterned Indian blankets cover the wall above the bed. On the three other crudely plastered, make-shift walls hang crucifixes, nineteenth-century family photographs, a Russian icon, religious pennants and scrolls (including images of the Virgin), etc. On the wall, screen left, there are three empty picture frames suspended from a nail; CARL's long black coat hangs from an adjacent nail. There are old books on the floor and under the bed, a plate, shoes, and remnants of several of CARL's collections: shells, rocks, driftwood. (Not visible in this shot—but they will be glimpsed in later shots—are a Buddha, some cooking utensils, and a portable kerosene stove.)

Seeing LENA, CARL acts very alarmed. He quickly stands up on the bed, his back pressed hard against the wall, breathing noisily. The ceiling is too low for him to stand up completely straight. He is wearing his baggy tan pants and a light-colored shirt unbuttoned at the wrists.

Closer (medium) shot of CARL: his head and the upper part of his body.

Back to wider shot (camera is behind and to the right of LENA). LENA approaches the bed. When she sits on it, the camera tilts down with her; now we see CARL only from the waist down. LENA looks up at him.

LENA

Sit. Sit next to me.

Slowly, CARL descends—keeping his back rigid against the wall —until he comes to a squatting position on the bed behind LENA (thus putting all of himself in the frame). He seems less frightened, though still wary; his breathing is quieter. LENA reaches out and touches CARL's face. He flinches and turns his head away. She puts her hand to his cheek again, strokes it.

LENA

Let me.

This time he endures it, his face a blank. She takes her hand away. He reaches out and puts it back against his cheek. (Camera is in medium shot here.) At the moment CARL seizes LENA's hand, the lyrical theme being played on the flute is taken over and developed by a string quartet.

LENA draws her hand down CARL's face to his neck, then puts her hand inside his shirt and starts caressing his chest. He lets her do it. She starts undoing the buttons on his shirt. When she takes it off, he cooperates by moving his back away from the wall. Then she takes the string belt of his trousers and starts untying it. CARL pulls away violently and stands up on the bed, his back against the wall (again, only his body from the waist down remains in the shot), but LENA continues what she was about to do, almost without pause, not having let go of CARL's belt when he stood up. When, from this position, she undoes the top buttons of his fly and starts to pull down his trousers, CARL offers no resistance.

Change of shot: CARL's left thigh occupies the right foreground of the image. To the left, mid-ground, is LENA's face, looking up at CARL's face (off-screen) while she pulls down his trousers. When CARL's trousers are at his ankles, she pauses, leaning her head for a moment—almost wearily—against his thigh. But when she then reaches up for his underpants, he convulsively grips her hand to stop her, then lets go and backs away.

Full shot of CARL moving along the wall. He frees himself from his trousers, then slowly lowers himself into a sitting position. Glancing down at the bunched trousers beside them, he picks them up and throws them on the floor. He sits pensively for a moment—knees bent, his left hand clasping his left shin. Then he lies back slowly (his head is screen right) and inserts himself under the blankets, painstakingly drawing one about himself up to the chin. Only then does he look at LENA.

Wider shot, from a side angle, of LENA. She has been watching him. She sighs, then starts to take off her sweater. She stands up, at the same moment quickly pulling it over her head. (Underneath she is wearing the top of a black two-piece

bathing suit.) Moving to the center of the tiny space, she slips off her pants. About to take off her underpants (the bottom part of the swimsuit, actually)—she has her thumbs already hooked in the waistband—she looks back at CARL (off-screen) and thinks better of it. Leaving them on, she turns and comes back to the bed.

Change of shot: camera near the doorway for as wide a shot as possible. Reaching the bed, LENA gets on top of CARL, then pulls a blanket over them both. She embraces CARL, which he allows passively. But when she tries to kiss him, holding his head in her hands, he turns his face away. After a few moments of struggle, she stops trying to kiss him. She puts her right hand under the blanket but obviously doesn't find any signs that he's on the way to being aroused.

Close shot, which favors LENA: camera is below LENA, just to the left of CARL's head.

LENA

(*Whispering*) What can I do?

Another close shot, almost reverse angle (camera is behind and to the right of LENA): looking down at CARL's face. He shakes his head for an answer. Music ends.

Wider shot. LENA moves off CARL to lie at his side (nearer the wall), propped up on one elbow. CARL is now in the foreground. They are covered by blankets. LENA bends over CARL's torso, gets on top of him again, and slides her body downwards. Just as her head is about to disappear under the blanket, CARL grabs her roughly by the hair to stop her, and pulls her up so that she is again stretched out along the length of his body. She gazes at him sadly.

LENA

Tell me what you'd like.

Another medium shot. CARL shakes his head. LENA, seen more frontally, puts her face very near his.

LENA

Shall I talk? About what a woman likes?

Again CARL shakes his head.

LENA

No? . . . I'll tell you about other men I've been with.
What they did.

CARL shakes his head more emphatically. LENA looks intently
at him.

LENA

There must be something.

CARL, staring at her, wets his lips.

CARL

Are you willing . . . to go . . . very . . . far?

LENA is startled, and takes a moment before answering.

LENA

Let's go . . . very far.

CARL moves convulsively to get on top of LENA, getting tangled
up in the blankets.

New shot; the camera is low, and behind CARL. He thrashes
about in a painful parody of love-making—groaning, wincing,
grinding his teeth. Still impotent, he finally rolls off her.

Wider shot (from LENA's point of view) of CARL only. CARL's
torso rises into the shot, away from LENA's body; he almost
hurls his back against the wall at what is now the foot of the
bed. (It was the head of the bed in the first shots of this
sequence.) CARL pulls the blanket up around his waist, as if to
protect himself.

Reverse angle shot of LENA only. LENA, on her back, stares at CARL (off-screen). Suddenly she sits up; the camera (in roughly CARL's position) pulls back. She rips off the top she has kept on all this time, then lies back again. We see her breasts for a moment; then the camera moves in closer to her face.

LENA

Hurt me!

Medium shot taken from the head of the bed (roughly LENA's point of view). CARL is kneeling at the foot of the bed, midground, facing frontally. He looks down at LENA (off-screen) with a particularly sad expression.

CARL

Martin has made you bad, too.

Medium close shot of LENA, from CARL's point of view. She looks frightened.

LENA

You can kill me.

Back to medium shot of CARL. On these words his expression changes and he throws himself toward LENA (i.e., toward the camera).

Wide shot, taken from the side of the bed. CARL, on top of LENA, pulls the blanket over them. Then he begins to make love in a new way—a way not yet fully genital but both sensual and very tender. At first LENA seems to welcome CARL's lovemaking—they are making love to each other—but as it goes on, she becomes passive, then absent. CARL continues. (Because of the limited space of the cabin, this has to be shot, like much of this sequence, with a hand-held camera and will consist of several shots.) Sound of the door opening. LENA looks up.

Full shot (from the viewpoint of LENA and CARL) of MARTIN standing in the doorway. He is wearing a striped cotton shirt and corduroy trousers, and he holds a flashlight before him.

MARTIN

Don't get up.

His voice is calm.

Full shot of the bed. LENA jerks away from CARL, who, partly raised on the bed, glances over his shoulder, then falls back, inert. LENA sits up and pulls a blanket away from him to hold it against the front of her body with one hand. She looks off-screen (at MARTIN), then down at the lifeless-looking CARL, then back again at MARTIN.

43. The kitchen and music room of Martin's cottage. A little later

Wide shot: in the foreground is MARTIN (his back to the camera), sitting at the small kitchen table, drinking coffee. He is wearing the same clothes as in the next-to-the-last shot in the preceding sequence. Mid-ground—in MARTIN's direct line of vision—is a doorway (no door); in the background is the fourth room of MARTIN's four-room cottage, in which there is a piano, a violin, some flutes and recorders, a hi-fi set, and shelves of records. As the sequence begins, we hear the sound of foot-steps. A second later, LENA enters. She remains in the other room—that is, in the rear of the shot. She circles back and forth in the room, snapping her fingers; then she puts on a record (a Swedish group called Quiet Grave) and begins to dance by herself. Not moving (so his back is still to the camera), MARTIN calls out, over the music.

MARTIN

Is Carl all right?

LENA answers him without breaking her step, barely looking
at him from the other room, in a tone as dissociated as his own.

LENA

He seemed asleep when I left.

She continues dancing.

MARTIN

Good.

MARTIN gets up, and says his next words as he leaves the shot
on the left side of the frame. (He is going to get some coffee
for LENA.)

MARTIN

Then he wasn't—

Several seconds of the rattling of cups and spoons. As MARTIN
reenters the shot from the left, carrying a steaming cup of
coffee, he finishes the sentence.

MARTIN

—too upset by my coming in on you.

MARTIN sets the cup down on the kitchen table where he has
been sitting. LENA, in the rear of the shot, does not acknowledge that he has said anything. She goes on dancing. Then,
again without breaking her step, she says something. (She has
to shout to be heard over the music.)

LENA

He asked me about his letter.

Change of shot, reverse angle. The camera is now in the music
room, behind LENA—seen in half figure, facing screen right.

She goes on dancing, staying more or less in one place, her head down. In the background of the shot, through the doorway, we see MARTIN in full figure, standing next to the kitchen table (which is screen left). The cut to this shot comes exactly after LENA says the word "letter." At the mention of this letter, MARTIN comes agitatedly to attention.

                    MARTIN
   A letter Carl wrote me?

LENA, dancing in the foreground of the shot, answers matter-of-factly.

                    LENA
   He wanted me to give it to you.

MARTIN hurries into the music room toward LENA (toward the camera); when he reaches her, they are both in medium shot. He looks transfixed.

                    MARTIN
   Where is it?

LENA, still dancing and partly turned away from MARTIN (who is beside her, facing the camera), replies in a flippant tone.

                    LENA
   I tore it up.

MARTIN grabs LENA's shoulders and spins her around to face him. (We now see only the back of her head and a quarter of her face.)

                    MARTIN
   I've been waiting for that letter for five years!

LENA stares at MARTIN without flinching, frightened but defiant. She doesn't answer. He speaks very agitatedly.

MARTIN

Did you read it? What did he say?

Reverse angle: medium shot, with the camera behind MARTIN. We see the back of MARTIN's head and a quarter of his face, and LENA, eyes blazing, in full face.

LENA

I'll never tell you. I'd rather die than tell you!

She pulls away from MARTIN and walks past him, out of the shot. MARTIN turns around—now he is facing the camera—and watches LENA (off-screen) go into the kitchen. He looks nonplused.

Reverse angle shot, from MARTIN's point of view. We see LENA go through the doorway into the kitchen and stand next to the kitchen table (in full figure, facing screen left), putting some sugar in her cup of coffee and stirring it. MARTIN enters the shot: he crosses the threshold, goes to the far side of the kitchen table, sits down—the same place he was sitting at the beginning of the sequence—and folds his hands. Now he is again seen frontally. He looks up at her expectantly. LENA, still standing in the same place, sips some coffee, without looking at him. Her hands are trembling.

LENA

It's true, then.

MARTIN looks down.

MARTIN

You don't understand—I can't explain . . .

LENA looks stricken. Holding her cup, she turns and takes a few steps away from MARTIN (i.e., toward the camera). She is going back into the other room. MARTIN looks up. His tone is pleading.

128

Don't go.

Pausing in the doorway, LENA half turns. Standing there, she is again facing screen left. We see MARTIN clearly in the background, in the left side of the frame, at the kitchen table.

LENA

How *could* you?

MARTIN

Let's stop torturing each other . . .

He makes a gesture inviting her to join him, to sit opposite him at the kitchen table. LENA's reply is to turn back (so she is seen more frontally) and continue into the other room. She walks out of the shot on the left side of the frame.

New shot: the camera, in the center of the music room, picks up LENA (seen from behind) going toward a small table in the music room. This table, same size as the one in the kitchen, also with two chairs facing each other, is set against the wall of this room exactly as the other table is set against the corresponding wall in the kitchen. (Note: MARTIN's cottage is square and is divided into four rooms of identical dimensions.) LENA sits down in the chair equivalent to the one in which she would have been sitting had she stayed with MARTIN in the kitchen. Trembling, she sets down the cup and saucer. Against the wall to her left (i.e., between her chair and the wall) is a large photographic blowup of the head of a bald, thin-faced man with a small beard, who seems to have a skull fracture—a kind of death's-head; LENA's head, now seen in right profile, is in the middle of the photograph. Once seated, LENA is now, so to speak, facing MARTIN—although she cannot see MARTIN nor can he see her. Looking straight ahead (i.e., screen right), she sees (off-screen) the spinet which stands against the left portion of the wall that the music room and the kitchen have in common. (The doorway connecting the two rooms is in the middle of that wall, like the other three

doorways in the cottage.) She looks down, then up—in MARTIN's
direction.

LENA

I hate you for not caring that I went to bed with Carl!
(*Pause*)
I understand what's going on. It's Karen.

Camera pans slowly to the right: leaving the table (so that
LENA is excluded from the shot), passing over the wall and the
spinet until MARTIN, seen through the doorway connecting the
music room and the kitchen, occupies the center of the shot.
He is looking in LENA's direction.

MARTIN

What I like about Karen is that she's not finished.
There's so much life in her she doesn't even know
about . . .

MARTIN pauses, waiting for LENA's reply.

Cut to still shot of LENA, in right profile, at the table in the
music room (same camera position and framing as in the previous shot, before the pan). She stares straight ahead, i.e.,
screen right.

Back to long shot of MARTIN at the table in the kitchen (same
camera position and framing as in the previous shot, after the
pan). He sighs, stands, picks up his cup and saucer, and comes
into the music room. The camera pans with him, from right to
left—the reverse of the previous pan. Music (of record LENA put
on) fades. MARTIN reaches the table where LENA is, sits in the
chair opposite her (twin to the chair in which he was sitting
in the kitchen), and sets down his coffee. His face is more
remote now. LENA leans forward.

130

LENA
And how much life do I have? What reason do I have to live if you don't want me?

MARTIN doesn't answer.

LENA
Give me a reason . . .

MARTIN looks at her.

MARTIN
I want you to live, but I can't give you any reasons.

LENA
(*Bitterly*) You could remind me how talented I am. Tell me that I mustn't throw away such talents.

MARTIN
But I don't believe that's a reason.

LENA
You needn't say just what you believe!

MARTIN, irritated, rises from his chair to cut off the conversation. He takes a few steps away from LENA (i.e., toward the camera); she reaches out and grasps his bare forearm. He stops. MARTIN's head has been excluded from the shot. His torso is in the foreground; behind him and to his right (screen left) is LENA's face and the upper part of her body. Holding on to his arm with both hands, she looks up imploringly at MARTIN's face (off-screen).

LENA

Touch me.

▼ *44. Grounds of hotel. Still later: almost dawn*

Long shot of the hotel grounds. A gardener is watering some bushes in the left foreground. Sound of birds.

Very long shot. LENA walks across the deserted lawn. The gardener is in the far background. Camera tracks forward slowly as she nears the main rear entrance. Noise of an outboard motor. She goes inside.

45. Balcony and interior of hotel room.
   A little later

Full shot, low angle, of the balcony. LENA, wearing her glasses, still in the same black pants and sweater she has worn since sequence 32, is seated at a small table, writing on a sheet of paper. On the table is an envelope, a glass of water, a bottle of pills. Noise of an outboard motor (louder).

Close-up of LENA's hands as she puts down the pen and takes several pills out of the bottle. She holds them in her right palm. Noise of the outboard motor fades.

Long shot of the inside of the room—the camera is on the threshold of the balcony—with KAREN, asleep in her bed, in the center of the image.

Medium shot of LENA—the camera is on the far side of the table on the balcony—taking off her glasses. In the background: the open French doors leading into the room. LENA folds the paper, puts it in an envelope (which she doesn't seal), then stands. Sound of birds.

Full shot, reverse angle—the camera is inside—of LENA coming through the doorway into the room (i.e., toward the camera). Sound of water running, then of a toilet flushing, from the bathroom of an adjacent room. The camera pans with LENA, keeping her in the center of the image as she moves to her left (screen right) to drop the letter on her unmade bed; at that moment, her back is to the camera. Pan stops: KAREN, asleep, is also in the shot, screen left. Without breaking her stride, LENA turns (so she is seen frontally again), walks toward the camera, then passes out of the left side of the frame. Several seconds go by. The sleeping KAREN does not move. Cut right after the sound of a door closing.

46. Beach. A little later: sunrise

Very long shot: sea, sky. Music. No natural sound.

Close-up of LENA's bare feet walking into the water. Music continues.

Long shot, from behind, of LENA entering the water. (Same beach as in sequence 19.) She goes in as far as her waist. Then

133

she turns around and comes out again (walking toward the camera). Natural sounds: the sea, wind, etc. The camera follows as LENA walks up and down the beach for a few moments. She seems cold. She looks around, as if she hoped that someone would appear to stop her. Toward the end of the shot, the music starts again. Sound of sea and wind continues.

Very long shot of the deserted beach. Music; sound of sea, wind.

Medium shot: LENA, seen from the waist up, returns to the water. The camera tracks forward, then stops. LENA, now seen in full shot, continues walking until the water is over her head. (This shot doesn't imitate the composition or framing of the shot in sequence 19 in which CARL walks into the water.) Music up; sound of sea, wind.

Another version of the first shot in this sequence. Silence.

47. *Music room of Martin's cottage. Later that morning*

The screen is completely filled by a sketch of two female dancers in black leotards. The drawing is rough: arrows indicating movements on the stage, etc. After a moment, MARTIN (seen from behind) stands up into the frame from below—only his head and upper torso—then goes out on the right. Footsteps. Music throughout the shot.

Long shot, high angle, of the side of the room where MARTIN has been making sketches for a new work. In the center of the image: a long table strewn with drawings, pencils, crayons, an ashtray with a still burning cigarette, etc. Propped up against the wall above the table is the big sketch—on 4' x 4' cardboard—seen in the previous shot; only the lower half is visible.

Music fades out at the beginning of this shot. Sound of a shutter banging in the wind.

48. *Rocks near the beach. Late that morning*

Three-quarter shot, low angle, of CARL. Convulsive music; loud natural sounds: wind, the sea. CARL is standing on a flat rock, his large blanket draped over his shoulders; he wears his light sweater and tan pants with the bottoms rolled up to mid-calf. CARL is looking down, toward the sea (i.e., toward the camera), an expression of horror on his face. Transfixed by what he sees, he opens and closes his mouth as if he wants to speak or scream, but no sound comes out. Music stops; wind, sea up. CARL flings off his blanket—it falls on the rocks below his bare feet (off-screen)—and pulls up the whistle that he always wears hanging from his belt. CARL starts blowing the whistle. As he blows, he looks wildly from side to side to see if anyone is coming. It is all somehow inept; one long blow of the whistle seems to exhaust him, and he pauses for several seconds before blowing again, without taking the whistle from his mouth, so that between the loud, shrill sounds there is a faint, asthmatic whistling sound (CARL's tortured breathing).

Very wide shot, high angle (from CARL's point of view), of the sea just below. LENA's body is floating face down in the shallow water near the rocks. Sound of CARL blowing his whistle for the length of the shot (at least twelve seconds).

Back to previous low-angle shot of CARL. He blows once more on his whistle, with less conviction this time, then lets it fall out of his mouth and hang again along his thigh. He starts forward (i.e., toward the camera) to get LENA.

Back to previous very wide shot, high angle: the camera is above and behind CARL as he descends the rocks, enters the water up to his knees. Being too thin to be very strong, he has

some difficulty lifting LENA up out of the water; then he catches her under the arms and drags her toward the rocks. Once he has dragged her body out of the water and onto the nearest flat rock, he reaches out for the blanket he discarded before, and covers her up to the shoulders.

Medium shot; the camera, very low, is on an adjacent rock on the same plane. LENA—her head (screen left) and the upper part of her body, covered by the blanket—lies in the foreground. We see her face in three-quarters view. CARL is mid-ground, crouching down by her left side.

Close-up, reverse angle (from CARL's point of view): LENA's white face with drops of water on it, her drenched blond hair, the neck of her black sweater. Her face is seen in left profile, turned away from the camera.

Back to medium shot: LENA lies in the foreground—the camera is very low—and CARL is mid-ground, crouching down on the other side of her body. Tears in his eyes, CARL stares incredulously at LENA.

136

CARL

Wake up.

He adjusts the blanket covering her, like a parent tucking a child in bed.

CARL

Don't be cold.

He gazes at LENA again. Then he bends over and puts his right cheek against her face.

CARL

(*Whispering*) You're good. (*Louder*) You're good.

He raises his head slightly, nods once or twice to himself.

CARL

You're good.

He looks down at her: a renewed surge of despair.

CARL

Wake up!

He waits a moment to see if this will have any effect.

CARL

(*In a hoarse whisper*) Wake up!

He waits another second, then moans.

CARL

(*Screaming*) Wake up!

He flings himself across the upper part of LENA's body, holding her tightly, almost covering her from view. With his face buried in her neck, he starts by shouting and ends by sobbing.

Wake up! Wake up! Wake up!

CARL draws himself off LENA's body, sits upright. Without taking his eyes from LENA, he reaches fumblingly for the whistle hanging from his belt and lifts it to his mouth. He blows on it —sobbing all the while—several times.

Very long shot, low angle, of MARTIN (dressed as in sequence 47—sweater and pants) coming at a run out of a wooded area behind and above the rocks where CARL is. Sound of whistle stops. The camera pans with him as he runs agilely down a path that leads from the promontory to the sea, and reaches CARL. CARL—crouching like an animal on the left side of LENA's body—looks up at him expectantly, dumbly. MARTIN squats next to LENA's right side and takes her wrist to feel for a pulse. He holds her wrist, alternately looking down at her and gazing out, in distraught vacancy, at the sea; never at CARL. CARL does not take his eyes off MARTIN's face. Then, slowly, MARTIN replaces LENA's right arm at her side. He doesn't move. He glances at CARL.

49. *Front room and veranda of Martin's cottage. That evening*

▼ Medium close-up of KAREN. She is shivering; she looks feverish. MARTIN's hand is stroking her forehead.

Wide two-shot: MARTIN and KAREN; the camera is near the front door. On the far side of the room, to the right of the doorway leading into the bedroom, MARTIN is rising from the arm of the big chair in which KAREN is huddled. Against the wall behind the chair is another large mounted photograph; it shows the head of a gaunt-faced man (seen in big close-up, three-quarters view)—the same man as in the photograph in the music room seen beside LENA's chair in sequence 43. KAREN wears pants and a dark sweater. MARTIN is in the same clothes as in sequences 47 and 48. He goes out of the shot. The sound of a window being closed. ▲

KAREN looks up.

KAREN

How could she be so stupid!

She stands, takes a few steps toward the center of the room.

KAREN

I want to shake her, to slap her face, to yell at her.

KAREN turns (screen left) and goes out of the shot.

Full shot of KAREN from another angle. When the shot starts, KAREN (her back to the camera), is approaching the doorway that connects the front room with the music room. Then she turns sharply and stops. She is facing MARTIN (who is off-screen)—that is, in the direction of the camera. Making rigid gestures in her effort to control herself, KAREN speaks in a broken, plaintive tone.

KAREN

Don't you think . . .

She takes a few steps toward MARTIN, i.e., toward the camera. The camera moves back and to the right, so as to include MARTIN—seated on the low table of sequence 16—in the shot.

KAREN

Don't you think she'd see now what a stupid thing it was? She'd be sorry now . . .

She stands in front of MARTIN, clenching her fists. There are tears in her eyes.

Wider shot, new angle: the camera is near the front door. KAREN sits down on the other side of MARTIN. Now she is seen more or less frontally. MARTIN, who is nearer to the camera, stays mostly in profile—facing screen left.

KAREN

I'm so angry with her I don't feel any grief yet.

MARTIN

I can't grieve. It's your grief that makes me feel Lena's death.

He pauses, turns to look at her for a moment.

MARTIN

You see, I *am* a monster.

Turning away, he smiles—a mixture of sadness, self-pity, and sarcasm.

MARTIN

It's not as easy to be a monster as you might think.

KAREN

(*Softly*) I know.

We hear a noise coming from outside. KAREN gives a nervous start.

KAREN

Did you hear? Maybe it's Carl.

She moves to get up, but MARTIN restrains her lightly with his right hand and rises himself. He goes toward the front door— i.e., toward the camera—and passes out of the shot. KAREN stands.

Full shot, reverse angle, from KAREN's point of view. Through the open front door, we see MARTIN on the veranda, looking rather perfunctorily about him.

Wide shot; the camera is outside, on the far end of the veranda. KAREN hurries through the front door onto the veranda before MARTIN can come indoors again. She goes to the railing and leans over, peering into the night. Then she turns back to MARTIN.

KAREN

Where *is* he? We can't leave him alone tonight.

MARTIN tries to calm her.

MARTIN

I'll look for him.

He starts toward the veranda steps (i.e., toward the camera). KAREN quickly overtakes him, and seizes his arm. She glares at him with rage.

KAREN

Wait! He's afraid of you.

50. In front of Carl's cabin. Day

Long shot: CARL digging his hole. (A sequel to sequences 38 ▼ and 40, as well as the prologue to 51.) He is wearing khaki trousers and a close-fitting black turtleneck sweater. CARL's cabin is in the background of the shot. The door is open, and we can see that the kerosene lamp is lit. Music from the beginning of the sequence, and throughout, plus natural sounds.

CARL climbs out of the hole, throws down his shovel, and goes

inside his cabin (and out of sight). Nothing happens for several
▲ moments.

CARL comes out of the cabin, his arms full of assorted possessions: a nineteenth-century family photograph, a heavy refer-
ence book, some shells, a statuette. His face has a strained,
overconcentrated expression. He comes toward the hole (i.e.,
toward the camera) and throws his things in. He looks down
with satisfaction, moistens his lips, then turns to go back to
his cabin.

Wide shot—the camera is to the side—of CARL emerging with
another load of possessions. (He moves from screen right to
left.) CARL carries a satin picture of the Sacred Heart and two
large empty picture frames (one oval, one square); he tosses
them in the hole. He turns to go back to the cabin.

Cut to full shot of CARL, on his third trip from the cabin to the
hole. He is dragging along a blanket, a sackful of dishes, and
his kerosene stove. The camera tilts down as CARL dumps them
in; they land with a huge clatter.

Medium shot, low angle; the camera is in the hole. CARL, seen
frontally, is squatting at the edge, almost simian in his posture.
He looks down, then about him. His gaze is wild. He seems to
be trying to keep from crying. He rubs his nose with the back
of his hand.

Cut to full shot of CARL, midway on his last trip from the cabin
(again moving from screen right to left). He holds a large
wooden crucifix with a Grünewaldish Christ. At the hole—
this is seen from the side—he stoops down and places the
crucifix on top of the pile. Then he takes his long black coat
(the one he wore in sequences 27, 28, and 31) and lays it
gently on top of the crucifix.

Full shot; camera is behind CARL, and the hole is mid-ground.
He kneels for a moment, staring into the hole, in some sense

142

satisfied with his work. Then he stands and picks up the shovel; he is going to fill in the hole. He takes a shovelful of earth from a mound beside the hole and tosses it onto the coat. He takes a second shovelful of earth and throws it in.

Close-up: CARL's shovel entering the mound of earth a third time.

51. Cemetery in Stockholm. Two days later: morning

Close, high-angle shot of LENA's newly dug grave. It is completely covered with wreaths and flowers. Natural sounds throughout sequence, including sound of city traffic.

Very wide shot. On the far side of the grave, in full figure, are four mourners—from left to right: MARTIN, CARL, KAREN, PETER. MARTIN and PETER wear conventional black suits; KAREN wears a black dress, black boots, and a black angora cap; CARL has on his long black coat. Sound of airplane. They stand motionless for a moment, staring down at the grave. KAREN has a particularly grim expression; it seems to be mainly anger. CARL is rigid; his gaze is fixed, absent. After several moments, as if by common consent, PETER, KAREN, and MARTIN are all ready to leave. MARTIN takes CARL's arm. CARL stiffens, and tries to pull away.

CARL

Wait!

MARTIN

(Sternly) Can you bring Lena back?

CARL shakes his head, looks down at the ground. He no longer tries to escape from MARTIN's grasp. MARTIN starts leading CARL away (toward screen left). PETER turns to KAREN.

143

(*Softly*) Let's go.

KAREN turns to her right. She glances back once at the grave, as she starts walking; PETER moves to her right (farther from the camera). The four disappear behind the hedge on the left side of the image.

Very long shot, over a crowded field of old headstones, of the four mourners walking (from screen right to screen left) along the path that takes them out of the cemetery. CARL walks with MARTIN, who has his left arm in CARL's right arm. PETER and KAREN follow behind, not talking, not touching. Then MARTIN starts having trouble again with CARL; he is almost dragging him by the right arm now.

Closer shot (on the same axis as the preceding shot), which still shows the four in full figure. CARL takes a few more steps, then stops. He does not want to go any farther. MARTIN, a step in front of him, turns and tries to pull him along, but CARL will not be budged. KAREN and PETER continue just past them. Then KAREN turns around with a sharp movement to face CARL.

Medium close-up of KAREN, from CARL's point of view. KAREN's face and voice are distorted with violent feeling.

KAREN
There are no miracles, Carl.

Medium shot, reverse angle. CARL, seen past the back of KAREN's head and right cheek, looks frightened and defiant. His head rolls back as if KAREN had struck him; then he brings it forward again.

CARL
Yes, there are!

He wrenches himself from MARTIN's grasp and runs away (out of the shot), screen right.

144

Back to medium close-up of KAREN, appalled.

Very wide shot, like the second of this sequence; everyone is seen in full figure. We are back in the part of the cemetery where LENA is buried: the new grave is in the lower foreground. CARL runs into the shot from the far side of the hedge (the left side of the image). He circles around the grave, frenziedly stripping off the flowers and wreaths, tossing them about in all directions.

CARL

There are! There are! There are! There are!

MARTIN enters from behind the hedge. He runs toward CARL, seizes him, and drags him away from the grave. They struggle wordlessly for several moments, MARTIN screen left and CARL screen right. Then KAREN enters. She rushes over and tries to separate them, pulling at MARTIN.

KAREN

Don't hurt him!

CARL breaks away, leaving the shot on the right. (This action should be reminiscent of the shots in sequence 17, when MARTIN separated KAREN and CARL.) KAREN, extremely upset, turns angrily to MARTIN.

KAREN

He's not doing anything wrong.

52. *Bedroom in Sandler apartment. Ten days later: night*

Medium long shot. The camera pans from right to left over half the dark room to find KAREN and PETER in bed, asleep. Sound of the clock ticking. The camera—located beyond the foot of the bed—continues to pan, going past them. Then we hear (off) KAREN crying out.

Wide shot of the double bed from the side. Beyond the bed, on the opposite side of the room, is a window with a white curtain; there is a white blanket and white sheets on the bed. Whimpering sound. Mid-ground, KAREN stirs, then suddenly sits up, looking around as if she doesn't know where she is. She is wearing a white nightgown. She whimpers. PETER (nearer to the camera) opens his eyes, raises his head.

PETER

What?

KAREN

I dreamed . . . I dreamed that Lena came back to life.

She throws herself on PETER's bare chest, lets herself be held tightly for a moment. Then she draws a little away from him to talk.

KAREN

She'd been dead for weeks, but I had her body with me. There was some reason why she couldn't be buried yet.

▼ Medium two-shot: KAREN and PETER. KAREN turns slightly away from PETER as she continues recounting the dream. PETER

146

slowly props himself up on his pillow; he does not take his eyes off KAREN.

> KAREN
> So I stayed on in the hotel.

PETER's arm goes out of the shot. A light goes on. (He switched on the lamp beside the bed.)

> KAREN
> It seemed natural that her body should be in my charge, and that it should lie there in the next bed . . . Then, one day . . . I was sitting near the window, reading . . . and I just happened to glance over at it. It wasn't so greenish white.

53. Stage of an old theatre in Stockholm. Indeterminate time

Very long shot of the bare stage. The camera, which is in the orchestra, tracks forward slowly. At the rear of the stage, MARTIN and KAREN are standing together. KAREN wears a dark wool midi-dress and boots; MARTIN has on pants and a white shirt. We are too far actually to be able to hear what KAREN is saying in low tones; we hear it as a voice-over.

> KAREN'S VOICE
> Without daring to think anything special was happening, I went over to look . . . Then I thought I saw her breast rise and fall.

KAREN moves toward the wings (screen left); MARTIN follows.

> KAREN'S VOICE
> As if she were breathing.

They stop.

Medium long shot of MARTIN and KAREN, with a piece of stage scenery—a grove of trees—behind them. KAREN pauses, breathing heavily. She has her back to MARTIN.

> KAREN
> I knelt down next to the bed—my heart was pounding—and I saw that her lips were trembling, and that there was pink in her cheeks.

She turns to face MARTIN.

> KAREN
> I still couldn't believe what was happening! . . . until I saw a tiny tear slip from under one eyelid and roll down her cheek. Then I knew . . .

She pauses.

Medium frontal shot of MARTIN, his face impassive.

> KAREN
> (*Off*) Gradually her breathing got stronger. She slowly opened her eyes.

54. *Bedroom in Sandler apartment. Same as sequence 52.*

Medium close shot of KAREN sitting up in bed. Her face is in three-quarters profile.

> KAREN
> She looked so tired, so frail. I went wild with joy. I raised her up . . . Holding her in my arms, I pleaded

with her to say she was sorry she'd killed herself—to say she was grateful for the miracle that had given her another chance to live.

She pauses, turns to face the camera.

> KAREN
> Finally, in a very weak voice, she said she was glad to be alive. And I was satisfied.

KAREN lies back heavily, her head partly hanging over the far side of the bed.

Medium long shot of KAREN (who is nearer the camera) and PETER. The camera is beyond the foot of the bed. PETER moves toward KAREN (i.e., toward the camera); he bends over her.

> KAREN
> I was so happy . . . I've never felt such happiness.

There are tears in KAREN's eyes. PETER puts his right arm under her neck.

> PETER
> (*Softly*) You mustn't take the responsibility for Lena's death on yourself. I won't let you!

KAREN turns her face away (toward the camera).

> KAREN
> That's what Martin says . . .

▲

55. *Old theatre. Same as sequence 53*

Very wide shot of MARTIN and KAREN standing facing each other on opposite sides of the stage. The camera is in about the tenth row of the orchestra. MARTIN, his arms folded, is screen left; KAREN is screen right.

KAREN

When I first woke up, I thought it had really happened . . .

KAREN is close to tears again. She turns, goes down the four steps on the right side of the footlights, and sits on the velvet-covered ledge of the ornate box just below and to the right of the stage. MARTIN, following her with his eyes, doesn't move. He speaks in a loud, schoolteacherish tone.

MARTIN

It wasn't really a dream about Lena. She stands for you, and you're describing your own resurrection.

KAREN stands, glares at him, and walks into the right aisle.

New shot, high angle, from MARTIN's point of view—the camera is now at the edge of the proscenium—of KAREN and part of the empty orchestra. Lights up. KAREN turns rapidly into the third row. Hurrying through the row from screen left to screen right, she looks up angrily at MARTIN (off-screen).

KAREN

(Shouting) But I *want* it to be about Lena! Why are you taking my dream away from me?

She stops in the middle of the row.

Full shot, low angle, from KAREN's point of view—the camera is in the orchestra—of MARTIN. He is standing on the stage next to the footlights.

MARTIN

What do you want? *You're* not responsible for Lena's death.

150

Back to previous high-angle shot, from MARTIN's point of view, of KAREN. Her tone becomes even more passionate.

> KAREN
>
> I want my dream.

She points to herself.

> KAREN
>
> I want my grief.

She continues through the row, shouting up bitterly at MARTIN (off-screen).

> KAREN
>
> I don't want to make a profit in wisdom from Lena's death!

She rushes toward the end of the row (right side of the frame).

56. Skansen Garden (Stockholm). Three weeks later: afternoon

Over several seconds of blackness, we hear KAREN and MARTIN speaking in quiet, intimate tones.

> MARTIN
>
> (Off) You've changed.

> KAREN
>
> (Off) Lena's death is heavy. I'm carrying it and I can't put it down.

Slow fade into a long shot of KAREN and MARTIN, walking in the garden. It is a compact, formal garden containing trees, hedges, and rosebushes—among which six small marble statues of

Renaissance-style *putti* are set at equidistant points. Coming toward the camera, they stop near one statue (seen to their right). KAREN is in the clothes of sequences 2 and 4; MARTIN wears his heavy brown wool sweater, a dark jacket, tan corduroy pants, and sneakers. The light is soft; the mood is elegiac. Natural sounds throughout.

MARTIN
You see how strong you are.

KAREN
I'm not strong . . . How can I be strong when I feel so guilty?

They walk on—the camera follows—then stop near another statue (seen to their left).

MARTIN
Survivors always feel guilty.

KAREN
They're right. To survive *is* to be guilty.

They walk some more, then stop just behind another statue. The camera doesn't follow this time.

KAREN
You want to make her death easier to bear than it should be.

MARTIN
Yes, I do. And it is . . . Be honest, it's already easier to bear than it was a week ago.

They walk again, toward a parapet—the garden overlooks the city—with the camera following them from behind.

KAREN
Yes . . . she's already disappearing.

Long shot, from another angle, of the garden, with the camera near the parapet. We hear footsteps; MARTIN and KAREN are approaching (but not yet in the shot). Sound of their footsteps on the gravel path is somewhat exaggerated.

MARTIN

(*Off*) It's all right. Some people have a duty to be happy.

KAREN

(*Off*) Not you.

Her voice is tender.

Now we see them, right mid-ground, walking toward the camera. They reach the parapet and sit down. The camera moves as they sit to put them just left of center in the frame, with the city behind them. MARTIN (screen left) is seen in profile, KAREN frontally.

MARTIN

No.

(*Pause*)

You're happy with Peter now.

KAREN

It's beginning . . . It's possible . . .

The camera tilts up on KAREN's words to show the city.

57. *Living room of Sandler apartment. Next afternoon, rain*

Full shot. KAREN is sitting on couch A, abstractedly playing with a toy of ANNA's; she wears the dark wool midi-dress and boots of sequences 53 and 55. PETER comes into the shot and sits beside her (on her left). He is wearing trousers, a white shirt, and a tie. KAREN puts down the toy, leans back. Natural sounds throughout sequence: heavy rain.

153

KAREN

I know you love me. But maybe we *can't* love each other.

Medium shot. PETER lies down—he is nearer the camera—and gently draws KAREN down alongside him. She smiles.

KAREN

Are you trying to seduce me?

PETER

If I open my arms very slowly . . .

The camera begins to track back slowly.

KAREN

People can't love when they're afraid of each other.

PETER

I'm not afraid. Are you?

KAREN

Yes. Of loving you badly . . .
(*Pause*)
No, not really afraid.

Medium shot again. They embrace. Sound of rain up.

PETER

Then you'll—

▲ She kisses him.

58. *Living room/dining room of Sandler apartment. Two weeks later: early evening*

Medium shot, frontal view, of ANNA, wearing a black turtleneck sweater and white underpants; she is playing with a book: hold-

154

ing it close to her right ear, listening avidly to the rustling of the pages. Then, from screen right, KAREN's arms encircle her in a warm embrace.

Long shot of the dining-room area, with the camera where couch A is. The round dining-room table is set for four. The meal is only half over; candles are still burning. PETER, alone at the table, in the chair screen right, is trying to eat. He wears the same clothes as in the preceding sequence, plus the suit jacket. Beyond the table, to PETER's right, is a bay window.

Wide shot, high angle—the camera is behind couch A—of a portion of the living room. In the left foreground, seen from behind, is CARL; he is sitting on the couch. ANNA and KAREN are on the living-room carpet; KAREN, on her knees, facing screen left, is right mid-ground; she is dressed as in sequences 53, 55, and 57. ANNA (seen frontally) drops her book. KAREN still has her arms around the child. ANNA stiffly extends her arms toward CARL. KAREN sees what she is doing and lets go. ANNA rises. KAREN pushes her gently toward CARL.

Closer shot (same axis as second shot of this sequence): PETER at the dining-room table. He glances at KAREN (off-screen)—i.e., toward the camera—and speaks with a trace of annoyance.

PETER

The child didn't finish. Bring her back.

Full shot, from KAREN's point of view, with PETER (partly visible) in the background of the shot, and CARL, on the couch, in the foreground. CARL, more normally dressed than we have ever seen him, wears a close-fitting white turtleneck sweater and grey trousers. CARL helps ANNA climb onto his lap. He looks at ANNA tenderly; she looks straight ahead. CARL takes two shells out of his left pants pocket—the two shells he picked up on the beach in sequence 19—and claps them together rhythmically. ANNA puts her head close to the shells and listens. He stops, then places the shells in her hands and smiles encouragingly. With-

155

out looking at the shells, ANNA opens her hands and lets the shells fall to the rug. (Same gesture as CARL dropping the flowers given him by LENA at the picnic in sequence 20.) CARL grins. He leans over and picks up the shells, pockets them—at the same time that he rises, carrying ANNA in his arms. Camera tilts up with him. He looks down at KAREN (off-screen).

CARL

You have to love her more to make the miracle.

He turns—walking around the couch—and goes back to the dining-room table. CARL sits down in the chair screen left; he sets ANNA on his lap and begins feeding her. The child lets herself be fed. PETER wipes his mouth with his napkin, gets up, and leaves the shot (screen right).

Medium frontal shot, high angle, of KAREN. She is still kneeling in the same place on the living-room floor.

> KAREN
> (*Softly*) Carl . . . ?

Medium shot of CARL—seen in right profile—at the table. He turns (toward the camera) to look at KAREN (off-screen).

> CARL
> You don't believe I can do one! . . . You'll see . . . God lets me do miracles sometimes.

ANNA's hand reaches up into the shot and takes the spoon from CARL. She throws it to the floor. The camera pulls back to show her sliding off CARL's lap and darting out of the room, screen left. (She leaves by the door behind CARL's chair.) CARL rises, turns to follow her. He looks in KAREN's direction.

> CARL
> Anybody can do a miracle.

He leaves the shot.

Back to medium shot, high angle, of KAREN kneeling on the living-room floor. PETER's legs enter the shot. He stands next to her, screen left—seen only to the waist. She looks up at his face (off-screen) lovingly.

> KAREN
> It's all right.

59. *Opera House (Stockholm): second floor. Next day*

Medium shot, low angle, of PETER. He stands on the left side of the frame, seen from the waist up; behind him are heavy, tasseled curtains—out of focus. He wears a light wool jacket, white shirt, tie, and dark slacks. Piano music, badly played, is heard from the beginning of the sequence to the end; the sound seems muffled. PETER appears uncomfortable; he speaks hesitantly. (This shot could—by being as nearly as possible the reverse angle of the final shot in sequence 58—suggest that he is speaking to KAREN.)

PETER

You know, I've always been . . . intimidated by you. I suppose it's my fault that—

Medium frontal shot of MARTIN. He is seated on an upholstered banquette at a small, round, white marble table. We are in one corner of the palatial gallery—empty now—on the second floor of the Opera, where refreshments are served before perform-ances and during intermissions. MARTIN is looking up quiz-zically at PETER (off-screen), i.e., screen left. He wears a striped shirt open at the neck, no tie; dark pants. It is, of course, MAR-TIN whom PETER was addressing in the first shot, and he con-tinues speaking, over the beginning of this shot, without a pause.

PETER

(*Off*)—we didn't meet years ago . . . when you were still married to Lena. Then, at the funeral—

MARTIN interrupts, his voice cool.

MARTIN

Am I as you imagined me?

PETER comes into the shot from the left and sits down uneasily next to MARTIN, on MARTIN's right (i.e., screen left).

PETER

I'd seen photographs of you, of course . . .

(*Pause*)
You look . . . smaller.

MARTIN appraises him ironically.

MARTIN

And older.

PETER looks embarrassed. MARTIN, still with his ironic expression, gets up, crosses in front of PETER, and goes to the little balcony. (PETER was standing on the left side of the curtained arch leading onto this balcony in the first shot.) The camera pulls back a little to keep them both in the shot. PETER, now on the right side of the image, turns to look at MARTIN. On the threshold of the balcony, MARTIN glances out at the grand staircase, a portion of which we see in the background, that goes down to the Opera lobby. Then he turns back to PETER.

MARTIN

Look, I thought I would have time to talk to you, but—

PETER

I could come later.

MARTIN

I don't know what good it will do.

He turns his back to PETER to look out from the balcony.

Very wide shot, with the camera where MARTIN is, on the balcony. On the left, the same floor, we see plain double doors at the rear of a broad landing with a railing which overlooks the lobby on the ground floor below; straight ahead is the grand staircase. As the shot starts, the doors swing open and out come two young women with long blond hair, both wearing black leotards; the repetitive piano music heard since the sequence started gets louder—it comes from a rehearsal room beyond those doors—then is muffled again when the doors swing shut. The two dancers exchange swift, affectionate glances. Laughing, one helps the other, who is carrying a parcel, into her duffel coat as, side by side, they gaily hurry, almost skipping, down the wide staircase. MARTIN and PETER continue talking over the shot.

MARTIN

(*Off*) There isn't anything I can do—to be honest, that I want to do—to help you with Carl.

PETER

(*Off*) Not help! I just thought—

MARTIN

(*Off*) How often does he come?

PETER

(*Off*) Well, you know . . . he likes the child, and—

Back to wide medium shot of PETER and MARTIN. PETER is still sitting at the small round table. MARTIN turns back to face him.

> MARTIN
> Does he ever talk about me?

> PETER
No.

PETER starts taking off his tie.

> MARTIN
Don't lie.

PETER stuffs his tie in the outside right pocket of his jacket.

> PETER
> Well . . . he gets angry . . . sometimes . . . when Karen mentions you.

> MARTIN
> Carl has a habit of adopting people. But if he really seems to have nowhere else to go, perhaps he should go back to the hospital.

PETER rises, as MARTIN continues.

> MARTIN
> There's a big trust fund for him, you know, that pays—

PETER advances toward MARTIN.

> PETER
> No, there's no reason for that! But Karen thought—

Again, the very wide shot, with the camera where MARTIN is, on the balcony: the staircase, the landing, and the double doors leading off to the left. The two dancers, having returned from wherever they went, are slowly, silently climbing the grand staircase. They don't look at each other. One is at least two steps ahead; the one, who follows dejectedly, trails her coat and shopping bag on the step below her. The mood now, the opposite of their exuberant mood before, is, almost caricaturally, 'after a quarrel.'

MARTIN

(*Off*) Listen, I must ask you to leave.

PETER

(*Off*) Are *you* all right?

There is no answer from MARTIN. Sound of footsteps. Meanwhile, we see the dancer who is ahead, after reaching the top of the staircase, cross the landing—in the rear left of the image —and stride through the swinging doors without holding them for her friend. (Piano music louder, when the doors open.) They close—music down—in the second dancer's face. She pushes the doors open again—music up—and goes through; they close, muffling the music again, behind her.

Medium long shot—with the camera, on another axis, still on the balcony—of MARTIN. From the left side of the image, MARTIN walks rapidly onto the landing. (During the dialogue-less second half of the preceding shot, he left the balcony and traversed the end of the gallery, leaving PETER behind.) He crosses the landing, then stops near the railing. Beyond MARTIN now, ahead and to his left (screen right), are the double doors through which the two dancers went. He turns to his right to look back at PETER (off-screen), i.e., in the direction of the camera. His tone is harsh.

MARTIN

Do you want to know, or are you asking for Karen?

PETER

(*Off*) I meant—

MARTIN cuts him off brusquely.

> MARTIN
> I must get back to my work.

He turns back from the railing (i.e., away from the camera) and starts toward the double doors.

Long shot, from MARTIN's point of view. We see PETER standing on the little balcony where MARTIN was before, hesitating. Then he reaches into his inside left jacket pocket and pulls out an envelope.

> PETER
> This morning Carl gave me this. For you.

> MARTIN
> (Off) Give it to me!

Astonished by MARTIN's shout, PETER turns and leaves the balcony—going out of the shot.

Back to preceding medium long shot; the camera is on the balcony. We see PETER enter the landing from the left side of the frame, as MARTIN had done, and cross the landing to join MARTIN. MARTIN grabs the letter from his hand and tears it open, ignoring PETER, who stands beside him on his right (screen left). MARTIN, facing the camera, advances nearer the railing and reads the letter agitatedly. He takes a few steps away—toward the double doors. Then he looks at the letter again.

Cut in very wide flash shot of exterior of the Rindö fort (similar to the third shot of the pre-credit sequence).

Return to medium long shot: MARTIN, not moving, his back to the camera, staring at the letter. He turns, comes back to where PETER is. His voice is grave.

> MARTIN
> Listen, you'd better get Karen.

PETER, mystified, doesn't move.

> PETER
> Why?

MARTIN touches him on the arm, then turns quickly to his left (screen right)—toward the grand staircase.

> MARTIN
> Don't worry. I know where he must have taken her.

PETER hurries after him. Camera pans to follow them.

> MARTIN
> There's a place he likes to go . . .

The two men run down the staircase. Cut just before they reach the bottom.

60. *Interior of an abandoned fort* (Rindö). *Later*

Long shot of CARL and ANNA (seen from behind); they are running, hand in hand, down a raked, vaulted space just inside the
fort. At the far end is the exit. It is dark; the light comes from
behind them. CARL is on ANNA's right. He is wearing the white
turtleneck sweater, grey pants, and shoes; no socks. She is wearing a short white dress with a dark vertical stripe on the left
side, low white socks, and shoes. (The first time we see ANNA
in a normal movement.) Echo of their footsteps. CARL pushes
open the great metal doors that lead out of the fort; there is
bright sunlight outside. They go through. The doors slam closed
with a loud, echoing bang.

61. *Near upper part of fort. About the same time*

Wide shot. From behind, we see KAREN, MARTIN, and PETER
hurrying along an overgrown path. To their right is a portion of
the curving wall of the fort. PETER is dressed as in sequence 59,
still tieless; MARTIN, in the same clothes as in sequence 59, has
added the dark jacket seen in sequence 56; KAREN wears a long-
sleeved, open-necked, beige top, a dark scarf, a tweed maxi-skirt,
and dark boots. Natural sounds.

62. *Near strand by fort. Moments later*

Wide shot of CARL and ANNA, who face each other; mid-ground
and screen left, part of the fort is visible. Behind them, a steep
hill—at the top of which MARTIN, KAREN, and PETER will even-
tually appear. CARL is kneeling in front of ANNA. He takes the
whistle that hangs from his belt and blows on it very softly.
ANNA, standing in front of him, cocks her head and listens.
(She is facing screen left.) After blowing the whistle, CARL
holds it to her ear. She listens, as if she still hears something.

Then, as if suddenly distracted, CARL rises. He takes ANNA by the hand and walks back up an incline toward the near wall of the fort. The camera pans to the left, to follow them. ANNA walks with CARL, trustingly, sometimes looking up at him. CARL does not look down at her. Loud sound of water and wind throughout the shot.

63. *Side of upper part of fort. Same*

Another version of sequence 61. KAREN, MARTIN, and PETER—with MARTIN in the lead—are half running along the curved path that goes around the side of the fort. KAREN is short of breath. Natural sounds.

64. *Strand side of abandoned fort. Moments later*

Very wide shot. CARL, as if in a trance, is leading ANNA along
the lower wall of the fort. They move from screen right to
screen left, passing several of the cupboard-like rusty doors in
the wall, one of which CARL entered with ANNA in sequence 1.
ANNA follows—we have never seen her so docile before—just
managing to keep up with CARL. Abruptly, CARL stops; he presses
his back against the wall. He lets go of ANNA's hand, lifts his
face up. Music starts. There have been natural sounds—sea,
wind—from the beginning of the shot. ANNA halts, too. She
stands before CARL, her back to the camera, waiting. CARL puts
his right hand in front of his eyes.

Medium close shot of CARL against the wall, seen from the
waist up; his hand half shields his tormented face from the sunlight. The music (which continues through this shot and to the
end of the sequence) changes. CARL turns to his right (i.e.,
screen left), as if he were receiving a signal from that direction. Suddenly, he comes to himself and looks down.

Back to very wide shot. We see the small figure of ANNA, still
standing in front of CARL, tugging gently at the waistband of

his sweater to remind him of her presence. CARL bends over and picks her up. He carries the child, facing him, against his chest, back down the slope—diagonally, from screen left to screen right—toward the strand (i.e., in the direction of the camera), all the while gazing fixedly, wildly, into her eyes.

Medium shot, with the camera beside the water. CARL, stiffly holding ANNA aloft, is on the right half of the image. The camera pans a short way with him, from right to left, as he advances toward the water, never taking his eyes off the child's face. CARL is both terrifying and piteous. Very gently, he sets the child down at the edge of the strand—ANNA is now seen from behind—and sinks to his knees in front of her.

65. Top of the hill beside upper part of fort. Immediately after

Wide shot, slightly low angle, showing a kind of outdoor corridor—formed by the curved side of the fort (screen left) and an old stone wall (screen right) with girders at the entrance—through which MARTIN, KAREN, and PETER hurry into view at the top of the hill. They come to a sharp stop together: obviously all seeing, with relief, that ANNA is safe below, near the water, with CARL. MARTIN is screen left; KAREN, looking terribly strained, is screen right, a bit ahead of PETER. They don't move for a moment. Then MARTIN takes a tentative step forward, a stunned expression on his face. Natural sounds throughout the sequence. Sound of their steps—gravel on the ground, etc.—is exaggerated.

Medium shot of MARTIN, speaking more to himself than to the others.

MARTIN

He can't. He can't.

Full shot, tighter than first shot of sequence, of all three. PETER, just behind KAREN and to her left (screen right), has his customary look of stolid, well-meaning incomprehension.

> PETER
>
> What's he doing?

KAREN, on MARTIN's left (i.e., screen right), gazes in mounting bewilderment at the two figures at the bottom of the hill (off-screen), then takes a step forward, half stumbling as she does, to stand next to MARTIN.

> KAREN
>
> Martin?

Incredulous, MARTIN is staring ahead (toward the camera), at what CARL is doing (off-screen). PETER takes two steps forward, to put himself closer to KAREN.

PETER
Let's get her!

But he doesn't advance any farther. Ignoring PETER, MARTIN touches KAREN's right arm and speaks with hoarse intensity.

MARTIN
Don't go closer.

KAREN glances at MARTIN, then back down the hill (in the direction of the camera). She has begun to understand.

66. *Water's edge and hill by fort. Same*

▼ Long shot, high angle, from behind, of CARL carrying ANNA—making his way down three rough cement blocks to get as close as he can to the water. Natural sounds: sea, wind.

Medium close-up of CARL's legs, as he crouches on the lowest cement block. He remains still for a moment, then pivots. (We haven't seen ANNA yet in this shot. As CARL turns, the camera tilts up, showing the upper half of CARL's body—and ANNA in his arms. He sets ANNA down on the grass at the water's edge; then he steps up and sits on his heels before her. Natural sounds. Music (strings, percussion).

Medium shot of both, with the camera behind and to the right of CARL. He leans far over to the right and down, to dip his right hand in the water. ANNA waits patiently. CARL straightens up—partially blocking ANNA from view—and caressingly wets her face. ANNA offers no resistance to any of this. Music fades
▲ out toward end of shot. Natural sounds continue.

Medium shot, low angle, of CARL—from ANNA's point of view. He looks down at the child (i.e., toward the camera) and smiles crookedly at her, a grimace of terrible intensity.

Think! . . . Think!

CARL's face becomes less twisted for a moment, as he waits—and searches for a sign from ANNA. Then he tries again. He wets his lips, and passes his forefinger across his mouth.

CARL
And say! Say words . . .

He gazes beseechingly into ANNA's face.

Medium close-up, high angle, of ANNA—from CARL's point of view. She looks up at CARL: unmoved, apparently, but attentive in a way we have never seen her. She opens her mouth, then soundlessly closes it again.

Back to medium shot, low angle, of CARL. His mouth becomes more convulsed, his look even wilder and darker.

CARL
(Whispering) Say!

Back to medium close-up, high angle, of ANNA. Her face is impassive but not vacant. Then she breaks into a broad smile. A gurgling sound. She begins to laugh softly. Music.

Back to medium shot, low angle, of CARL. His eyes widen and his face creases with joy; his smile is beatific. We hear ANNA's laughter (off), growing heartier. He shakes his head once or twice, then throws it back in ecstasy. Looking down again at ANNA, tears in his eyes, he starts laughing, softly at first, then roaring with joy. Music.

Back to medium close-up, high angle, of ANNA: hardly moving —not taking her eyes off CARL—laughing. Music.

Extremely long shot, with the camera at the water's edge. In the foreground CARL (screen left) and ANNA (screen right)—head and upper torso only—face each other. Rising beyond CARL and ANNA—in the center of the image, seen between and framed by their heads—is the hill. Screen left is the long wall of the fort which follows the steep incline, and part of the lower fort. At the top of the hill we see three tiny figures—MARTIN, KAREN, and PETER—with the curving rear wall of the fort behind them, and the high stone wall screen right. CARL, shaking with bursts of delighted laughter, tilts his head forward and blocks out the three tiny figures on the hill. Music.

Medium close shot of KAREN and PETER: the camera is just below them, at the top of the hill. KAREN in her distress opens her mouth as if to speak, but no words come out. Slowly she raises her right hand to her face. (She wears a ring LENA always wore.) She touches her lips, a gesture that resembles CARL's, several shots ago. PETER, behind her and to her left (screen right), stares without comprehending.

Medium long shot of CARL and ANNA: the camera is near the water's edge, several feet behind ANNA. We see CARL frontally, just on the other side of ANNA. Still laughing joyously, he glances up to his left (screen right) and spots the three figures on the top of the hill. As he sees them, his laughter dies. CARL realizes he has been observed; the spell is broken. Music changes. Appalled, confused, he glances down at ANNA, then looks up again to his left; he knows that those who are now watchers will soon descend to reclaim the child. ANNA, seen from behind, continues laughing softly. CARL's face becomes vacant. Suddenly, in one movement, he throws up his arms and seems both to collapse and to hurl himself toward the child (and toward the camera): in the way he flung himself forward on LENA in his bed, in sequence 42. Music up.

Wide shot, high angle, of CARL and ANNA, with an expanse of water behind them. The camera is back from and slightly behind CARL. His arms flung outward, CARL falls on top of ANNA—toward screen left—covering the child completely with his body. (CARL lies parallel to the edge of the strand—his right side near the water, his left side near the camera.) His head is screen left. Music continues up.

Medium long shot—camera on top of the hill—of MARTIN, KAREN, and PETER. PETER is the first to move forward, just ahead of KAREN. She seizes his arm and screams.

KAREN

Wait!

Nobody moves. Then KAREN shouts.

KAREN

Anna!

(The first time we have heard the child's name uttered.)

Back to wide shot, high angle, of the inert CARL, lying face down on the ground, ANNA on her back beneath him (almost hidden from view). After several moments the child starts

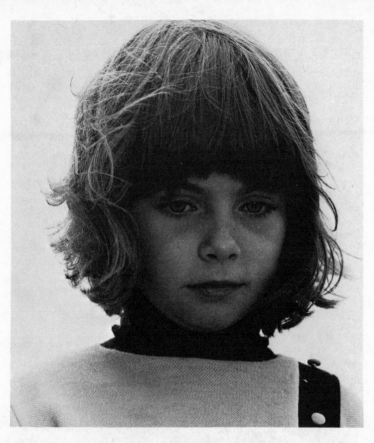

wriggling out from under CARL. He doesn't move. She rises; we see her from the back. Music continues up.

Medium close-up, low angle (reverse angle of the previous shot), the camera where CARL is. ANNA's head and shoulders, seen frontally, rise into the frame. The music stops. ANNA gazes tranquilly down at CARL. For the first time in the film, ANNA's face has a normal expression.

ANNA

He's heavy.

Back to wide shot of ANNA (seen from the back) and CARL, lying inert, prone. Music (string quartet—cello prominent) starts again, very emphatic. Groaning, CARL rolls over convulsively and lies on his back, then becomes catatonic. His eyes are open but blank; he is breathing heavily.

Back to medium long shot, brief, of MARTIN, KAREN, and PETER. KAREN's eyes are flaming with excitement. MARTIN, standing apart from the other two, looks stricken. He alone knows what CARL has done, given, and at what cost to himself: that CARL is lost.

Medium close shot of MARTIN, racked by anguish over CARL's fate and contempt for KAREN and PETER. He turns to the couple (off-screen right).

> MARTIN
>
> Help him! Damn you!

Wide shot, slightly low angle, of all three; camera is near the top of the hill, facing them. KAREN and PETER, seen in three-quarters figure, start down the hill at a run (toward the camera), going out of the shot in the right foreground—leaving MARTIN alone in the shot, gazing after them.

> KAREN
>
> (*Off*) Anna! Anna!

Very long shot, with the camera behind KAREN and PETER, near the top of the hill—i.e., from MARTIN's point of view. They continue running down the hill (away from the camera). KAREN has her arms open. Music (string quartet) up—to the end of the shot. At the bottom, we see ANNA, head lowered, pacing back and forth along the near (right) side of the unmoving CARL. When KAREN and PETER are two-thirds down the hill, she turns (in the camera's direction) and walks several steps away from CARL's body (diagonally, toward screen left); but she does not look up, or give any sign of noticing her parents approaching her. Music to crescendo. KAREN and PETER reach the bottom of the hill. KAREN, slightly ahead of PETER, falls to her knees and folds the child in her arms. PETER arrives a second later. Cut as he crouches down beside them. Music stops.

After a second's silence, fast syncopated drum roll. On a black screen, the names of the six actors and their roles in white letters.